Contents

Section 4 Further information

List of tables

List of figures

List of plates

Preface

This Bulletin has been written to give up-to-date practical advice to people involved in the reclamation of disturbed land who wish to plant trees on the restored site. Previous Forestry Authority recommendations on reclaiming land were set out in *A guide to the reclamation of mineral workings for forestry* (Forestry Commission Research and Development Paper 141). That report was commissioned by the Department of the Environment in 1983 because of the need to provide guidance under the powers introduced by the Town and Country Planning (Minerals) Act 1981. The report was published in 1985; over 1800 copies have been taken up, testifying to the interest in the subject within the minerals industry.

The 1985 report was mainly based on techniques tried and tested in the 1970s. Since then, considerable research has been undertaken by the Forestry Commission and others to improve tree performance on land disturbed by mineral workings. In addition, the Commission has had the unique opportunity to put into practice the fruits of research work, particularly on opencast coal, sand and gravel, and china clay mineral sites; some useful experience has also been gained on the afforestation of domestic landfill sites. A revision of guidance on these subjects has therefore been undertaken.

Land-use issues have become very important since the publication of the 1985 report. Agricultural surpluses have meant a wholesale re-appraisal of land-use in Britain, and a steady expansion of forestry is a major aim of the Government's forestry policy. For land reclaimed after mineral working, dereliction or landfilling, there is now a widespread feeling that woodland is a very appropriate after use. The need to improve the appearance and recreational value of land in and around urban areas has encouraged tree planting in community forests, often on degraded land requiring reclamation. The Government's Derelict Land Grant policy recognises the importance of reclaiming this type of derelict land for woodland.

Within the forestry industry there have also been changes in policy. Forests should now meet a range of objectives which include improving the appearance of the landscape, presenting opportunities for recreation and for public access to the countryside, and providing wildlife habitats as well as timber production. This Bulletin reflects these changes; it gives advice on how restoring disturbed or mineral sites for forestry can be an opportunity to maximise the diversity of the new forest landscape.

The structure of the Bulletin is similar to that adopted for the 1985 Guide, and concentrates on the reclamation of mineral workings to forestry.

However, many of the techniques described are just as relevant to the reclamation of other disturbed ground, such as derelict land or sites of waste disposal. These site types will be of particular interest to people working to increase woodland cover in urban and urban fringe areas, especially in the designated community forests. The guidance will be generally applicable wherever tree planting is planned, for forestry or amenity purposes.

The Bulletin is divided into four sections. The first is an introduction dealing with general reclamation issues. It includes a discussion of the extent of disturbed land and the value of its reclamation for woodland. Like its predecessor, the Bulletin also contains a chapter which highlights some of the main problems that disturbed sites can pose during reclamation and tree establishment.

This is followed by a major section containing recommended techniques for the restoration of mineral workings and their subsequent aftercare. Successful reclamation usually depends on decisions made before mineral working takes place, and the Bulletin includes a chapter on issues that should be considered then.

The next section contains chapters where the special natures of derelict land and landfill sites are discussed with reference to reclamation for tree planting. Another chapter discusses, in some detail, the particular reclamation strategies for some of the important mineral sites, overburden and waste materials where tree establishment is a real possibility.

A final section of appendices includes restoration and aftercare checklists, a specimen tree planting contract and schedule appropriate to restored land, and a set of specimen conditions for planning permission where forestry is the proposed after use following mineral extraction.

This Bulletin provides a comprehensive guide both to mineral companies, in preparing planning applications which involve proposals for forestry, and to mineral planning authorities, in considering such applications. It is also a comprehensive basis on which to plan the reclamation of derelict and other disturbed sites for tree planting. The Bulletin will facilitate the statutory consultations between mineral planning authorities and the Forestry Authority, and help people applying for support under the Forestry Commission Woodland Grant Scheme for tree planting on disturbed land.

La mise en valeur des terrains perturbés à des fins forestières

Résumé

Ce Bulletin donne les conseils d'ordre pratique les plus récemment formulés sur la plantation d'arbres en terrains mis en valeur et restitués. Il se concentre sur la mise en valeur des sites d'extraction minière à des fins forestières, mais un grand nombre des techniques décrites conviennent tout autant à la mise en valeur d'autres terrains perturbé, comme le relais et les sites d'évacuation des déchets. Ces conseils seront généralement applicables partout où la plantation d'arbres est prévue à des fins forestières ou dans un but d'aménagement.

Ce Bulletin est divisé en quatre sections dont la première est une introduction traitant de questions se rapportant à la mise en valeur en général. Elle comprend un examen de l'étendue des terrains perturbés et de la valeur de leur restitution à des fins forestières. On y trouve aussi un chapitre soulignant certains problèmes principaux pouvant être posés par les sites perturbés pendant leur mise en valeur et lors de l'établissement des arbres.

Vient ensuite une section principale contenant les techniques recommandées à la fois pour la mise en valeur des sites d'extraction minière et leur entretien ultérieur. Comme le succès de la mise en valeur dépend d'habitude de décisions prises avant que l'extraction minière ne s'effectue, cette section comprend un chapitre traitant de questions qui devraient être prises en considération à ce stade.

La section suivante contient des chapitres examinant les caractéristiques présentées par les relais et les sites d'évacuation des déchets, vues dans le cadre d'une mise en valeur ayant pour objectif la plantation d'arbres. Un autre chapitre analyse en détail les stratégies de mise valeur particulières se rapportant à d'importants sites d'extraction minière, de décharge et d'évacuation des déchets, présentant de réelles possibilités pour l'établissement d'arbres.

Une section finale regroupant des appendices contient des listes de contrôle ayant trait à la restitution et à l'entretien, un exemple de contrat se rapportant à la plantation d'arbres et un exemple de programme approprié aux terrains restitués, ainsi qu'un ensemble de conditions types devant être remplies pour obtenir l'autorisation requise, lorsqu'il est proposé qu'une utilisation forestière du terrain fasse suite à l'extraction minière.

Die Wiederurbarmachung von gestörtem Grund für die Forstwirtschaft

Zusammenfassung

Dieses Bulletin gibt aktuellen, praktischen Rat fur die Pflanzung von Bäumen auf wiederurbar gemachtem und restauriertem Land. Es konzentriert sich auf die Urbarmachung von Mineralwerken für die Forstwirtschaft, aber viele der beschriebenen Verfahren sind ebenso bedeutend für die Kultivierung anderer gestörter Gründe, wie etwa vernachlässigtem Land oder Müllgruben. Die Anleitung ist generell anwendbar, wo auch immer Baumpflanzung geplant ist, sei es für forstwirtschaftliche oder öffentliche Zwecke.

Das Bulletin ist in 4 Sektionen unterteilt. Die erste ist eine Einführung, welche die allgemeinen Probleme der Urbarmachung behandelt. Sie beinhaltet eine Diskussion über den Ausmaß des gestörten Landes und den Wert seiner Kultivierung als Waldland. Hier ist auch ein Kapitel, welches einige der Hauptprobleme während der Urbarmachung und Aufforstung von gestörtem Gelände, hervorhebt.

Es folgt ein Hauptteil, der sowohl Verfahren für die Urbarmachung von Mineralwerken, als auch die darauffolgende Pflege vorschlägt. Erfolgreiche Wiederurbarmachung hängt gewöhnlich von Entschlüßen ab, die vor dem Beginn des Mineralstoffabbaues getroffen wurden. Diese Sektion enthält ein Kapitel über Punkte, die dann betrachtet werden sollten.

Die nächste Sektion enthält Kapitel, die die Besonderheiten von ver-nachlässigtem Land und Müllgruben in Bezug auf Kultivierung durch Aufforstung behandeln. Ein weiteres Kapitel befasst sich ausführlich mit den besonderen Kultivierungsstrategien, für einige der wichtigen Mineralienwerke, Überlastete und Abfallmatérialien, wo Baumetablierung eine wahre Möglichkeit ist.

Die Endsektion der Anhänge beinhaltet Restaurierungs- und Pflege-prüflisten, ein Muster eines Baumpflanzungsvertrages und -planes für restauriertes Land, und eine Reihe von Musterbedingungen für Planungs-erlaubnis wo Forstwirtschaft die vorgeschlagene Nutzung nach Mineralienabbau ist.

Section 1 – Reclamation issues

Chapter 1

Reclamation in the United Kingdom

Why reclaim?

The United Kingdom is a densely populated country – its land is precious. Nevertheless, the 1988 Derelict Land Survey recorded some 40 500 hectares (ha) of derelict land in England (Department of the Environment, 1991a); a similar exercise for Scotland identified almost 7400 ha (Scottish Office, 1990). These figures are large and describe land which is, to most intents and purposes, useless. Derelict land continues to be formed: for example, between 1982 and 1988 some 11 000 ha became derelict in England alone (Department of the Environment, 1991a).

As well as derelict land, large areas of land are being worked for minerals (see Plates 1–4). In 1988, about 67 000 ha in England were affected, either for surface mineral extraction (*c.* 53 000 ha) or related disposal of mineral wastes (*c.* 14 000 ha) (Department of the Environment, 1991b); in Wales, almost 11 000 ha were affected by mineral working or waste disposal (Welsh Office, 1991). Modern legislation means that the majority of the land affected by mineral workings now has conditions attached to the planning permission which should ensure proper reclamation to an appropriate after-use. However, for a sizeable amount of land in England (*c.* 47 000 ha), there was little or no control of reclamation conditions. Most is likely to become derelict once mineral working has ceased. Some of the main mineral types worked in Great Britain are shown in Figure 1.1.

Apart from the non-productive aspect of derelict land, there are other reasons why it is very undesirable. Derelict land can be dangerous; hazards include tip failure, the collapse of old buildings, the crumbling of quarry faces, or exposure of dangerous chemical contaminants. Some derelict sites pose a fire risk, and others may be potentially explosive. Derelict land is usually ugly. Its very nature detracts from the image of the surrounding neighbourhood; new industry and domestic housing are discouraged, further reducing the economic prosperity of the region.

Land affected by mineral workings or dereliction may support a vegetation cover, but it is rarely productive. Eventually, natural colonisation may lead to some form of woodland – though it may take decades, if it happens at all (Finegan, 1984) (see Plate 5). In most circumstances, it is unacceptable to leave despoiled land 'to nature', and intervention, in the form of reclamation, is necessary.

All these reasons account for the Government policy of derelict land reclamation. In the last 12 years, nearly £750 million has been spent by the Department of the Environment, local authorities and industry to reclaim over 157 000 ha of land in England (Department of the Environment, 1991a). This land is now returned to a beneficial use, either for a 'soft' end-use such as agriculture, forestry, amenity or nature conservation, or for a 'hard' end-use such as industry or housing.

Why reclaim to forestry?

There are many reasons to consider forestry as a land-use after the reclamation of derelict land or mineral workings. Now that alternatives to agriculture are being sought, it makes

Figure 1.1a

Figure 1.1b

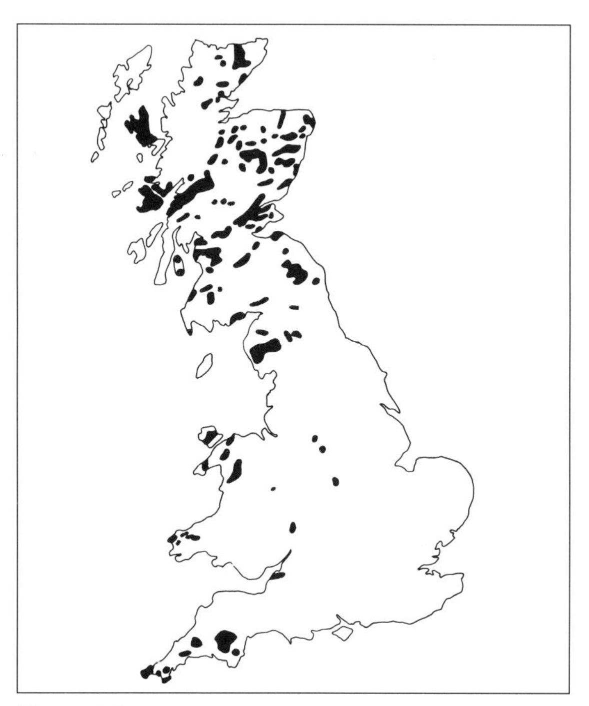

Figure 1.1c

Figure 1.1d

Figure 1.1 Areas of the country where some important minerals are derived: a. sandstone; b. limestone and chalk; c. igneous rock; d. sand and gravel.

more sense than ever to consider all the options – including forestry. Today, forestry is seen as a land-use offering many benefits besides timber production, including the enhancement of the landscape, and the provision of important habitats for forest flora and fauna. Forests also provide people with havens of peace and quiet to relax in and enjoy. In many areas, timber production, although still an ultimate objective, is secondary to some or all of the others mentioned here.

Woodland establishment after land reclamation may offer benefits additional and pertinent to those brought by general tree planting. These are the main benefits.

Timber production

Britain is one of the least forested countries in Europe – about 10% of its land surface is covered with woodland compared with a European average of 25%. As a result, Britain grows only about 10% of its timber needs, and imports nearly 50 million cubic metres of raw timber each year, costing nearly £7 billion. In 1990, only food, fuel and motor vehicles cost us more in imports (Forestry Commission, 1990). Reclamation to forestry may be seen, therefore, as an opportunity to contribute to the reduction of imports, albeit on a very small scale.

Reclaimed man-made sites can grow productive timber (see Plate 6). For example, many of the colliery spoil tips planted in the 1960s are now yielding useful timber products. On many sites, conifers, the more conventional timber-growing trees, will be entirely appropriate because, in general, they are well suited to sites which are likely to be infertile. However, broadleaved species, chosen increasingly for wildlife and aesthetic reasons, will also yield useful timber products such as wood for panel products, turnery, firewood, chips or pulp.

In many cases, woodland establishment, and management, can be supported by grants under the Woodland Grant Scheme (see Appendix 1). Returns from growing trees will depend to a large extent on site and crop, and on proximity to markets, current price levels and demand. However, on many properly reclaimed mineral and derelict sites, an economic return could be expected.

Wildlife habitats

Unreclaimed, mineral workings and derelict land can sometimes be valuable as wildlife habitats (Davis, 1976; Greenwood and Gemmell, 1978). In fact, some sites which have been colonized naturally and have become important as wildlife refuges may be chosen for preservation and conservation. In general, however, dereliction is now considered unacceptable, and reclamation usually desirable. Restoring land to forestry, or a mixed use including woodland, provides the ideal opportunity to plan and create important wildlife habitats – such opportunities are difficult to realise with hard end-uses, or agriculture. There are many examples of afforested reclaimed sites in the UK which are important in this way.

The Woorgreen reclaimed opencast coal site in the Forest of Dean is a good example of how sympathetic forestry reclamation has resulted in a valuable wildlife resource (see Plate 7 and Appendix 2). In South Wales, too, newly reclaimed sites are also important as wildlife habitats. Birds are attracted to recently reclaimed opencast coal sites before the trees reach canopy closure (Dawkins *et al.*, 1985) and many species make use of wetlands within areas of opencast land restored to forestry (see Plate 8).

The tree species commonly chosen as suitable for reclaimed land (see Chapter 6) can also add to its value for wildlife. On sites without topsoil, alders, birch, willows and rowan are the usual first choice for a planting scheme. These trees attract many birds. Coniferous woodland, too, can support important numbers of both common and rarer species of bird (Avery and Leslie, 1990).

Recreational opportunities

Forests are increasingly seen as important places for leisure-time activities (Benson and

Willis, 1991), a role recently accepted by the National Audit Office (1986). The joint Countryside Commission/Forestry Commission Community Forests Initiative, begun in 1990, has focused on the need for, and value of, woodlands in areas within and adjoining centres of urban population (see Figure 1.2). And many mineral and derelict sites are well placed to provide just such woodland when restored with trees.

There are some excellent examples of how reclamation sites can turn into valuable country parks after substantial tree planting. For instance, the Argoed Reclamation Scheme in the Afan Argoed Country Park, Gwent, shows how reclamation with, and amongst, trees can create beautiful areas for leisure and enjoyment (see Plate 9) (Reaney, 1990).

Figure 1.2 Location of community forests in England.

Community involvement

Planting trees on reclaimed derelict land close to built-up areas is an excellent way of involving the local community through, for example, community forest programmes. These are designed to encourage residents to be involved with their publicly owned trees. Better public relations, reduced levels of vandalism and greater accountability are all benefits of such involvement, but, in addition, residents develop a greater awareness and appreciation of, and sense of responsibility for, their trees. They become part of the decision making process that shapes their environment and can make an active contribution to it (Johnston, 1989). Participation in community forest activities can also have a beneficial effect on the social life of the community, improving social contact between residents and bringing them together in a creative atmosphere. Johnston (1989) describes further how the community can be actively involved in its local woodlands.

Landscape improvement

Derelict land and mineral sites are regarded by most people as eyesores. Even after reclamation, when soils are finally replaced, these areas often appear stark in the surrounding countryside. For engineering reasons, the appearance of the newly formed landscape is often unnatural. Drainage channels and roadways frequently cut into the otherwise smooth topography. Soil infertility can lead to inappropriate use of fertilisers, which again results in land with an unnatural appearance.

Large derelict land reclamation schemes now try to harmonize the improvement of the landscape over substantial areas. However, many mineral sites are surrounded by unrestored derelict land, or other mineral workings. Even if these sites are restored imaginatively, they can remain an oasis in an otherwise disturbed landscape. And, in phased mineral operations where mineral extraction on one part of the site can take place at the same time as restoration on another part, the final desired effect of reclamation may not be achieved until mineral extraction has ceased altogether.

Tree planting can help, often impressively, to reduce or eliminate these conflicts and criticisms. Fast-growing pioneer species can be used to screen remaining eyesores, for example creating shelterbelts around washeries or cement plants. Trees can also conceal mine spoil tips very effectively, without the need for expensive tip regrading. On restored sites, the textural amplitude of a woodland plantation will tend to obscure harsh engineered landforms or features, and will, if properly designed, promote good landscape links with the surrounding countryside or urbanization. Chapter 5 gives guidelines for the design of woodlands to be established on man-made sites.

Engineering considerations

There is an increasing appreciation that vegetation can perform an important engineering function. It has a direct influence on the soil both at the surface, where it protects and restrains soil materials, and at depth, increasing the strength and competence of the soil mass. Vegetation can also substantially affect soil moisture (Coppin and Richards, 1990). The effects of trees on a site are largely beneficial, and can be of considerable importance when planning the final land-use upon reclamation. This is especially so where site constraints such as topography and spoil materials make a safe engineered solution difficult to achieve. The box contains a list of the main site properties that trees may affect.

Costs

Establishment and maintenance costs of reclaiming derelict sites to a variety of soft end-uses (including woodland) have been reviewed for the Department of the Environment (Land Capability Consultants,

Engineering effects of trees

- **Rainfall interception**
  The degree of rainfall interception is somewhat determined by annual rainfall and its seasonal distribution. However, measured interception ratios of conifers in upland Britain vary from 0.19–0.62 (Maitland *et al.*, 1990); for broadleaved crops, interception ratios are generally smaller, ranging from 0.1–0.36 (Hall and Roberts, 1990). It is now generally accepted that conifers act to reduce water supply to the ground compared with grass or agricultural crops, and in certain parts of the UK broadleaves may also act in this way. In turn, a smaller water supply will lead to a reduction in water leaving the reclaimed site. This may be important where, for example, soil or spoil materials are susceptible to water erosion, or on landfill sites where the quantity of leachate production is directly related to the amount of effective rainfall (Chapter 8).
- **Storm hydrograph**
  Because of the canopy structure, the storm run-off hydrograph of streams issuing from a woodland cover is much less peaked, and run-off velocity is also reduced (Coppin and Richards, 1990).
- **Soil erosion**
  Woodland management is preferable to arable farming on substrates prone to water and wind erosion, because the tree cover generally acts to protect the soil. Care must be taken in the early years of establishment on sensitive materials, such as pulverised fuel ash (pfa) (Chapter 9).
- **Soil restraint**
  Roots of 1–12 mm diameter physically restrain soil particles from movement caused by gravity, water and wind. Trees are able to prop otherwise unstable or loose boulders and stones, preventing them from rolling downslope (Coppin and Richards, 1990).
- **Soil moisture depletion**
  Vegetation, including trees, can modify soil moisture content markedly, generally by reducing moisture content relative to unvegetated soil. The result is a reduction in pore-water pressure in saturated soils, and an increase in soil suction in unsaturated soil (Coppin and Richards, 1990).
- **Soil shear strength**
  Tree roots can markedly increase soil shear strength (Coppin and Richards, 1990).

1989). Table 1.1 gives the mean costs of reclamation schemes determined in their study. In general, the cost of restoring land to woodland cover is much less than for agriculture, recreation or public open space, mainly because expensive site levelling, topsoil importation and underdrainage are not required.

Table 1.1 Mean total cost of reclamation for different end uses (from Land Capability Consultants, 1989)

Land use	*Fig. 1.3 points*		*Total cost (£/ha)*
Public open space	Pos 1	<0.5 ha	47 100
	Pos 2	1–2 ha	14 400
	Pos 3	5–10 ha	11 500
	Pos 4	>10 ha	9 100
Agriculture	Agric		16 700
Woodland	Wood		10 000
Nature conservation	Nat		4 100
Recreation	Rec		24 400
Mixed	Mixed		12 000

Maintenance costs are also comparatively small compared with other land uses. Figure 1.3 shows the size of gross annual maintenance costs, and the relationship with establishment costs. It is interesting that there is a general relationship between the two types of cost, with small public open space and recreation schemes both expensive to create and maintain. However, annual maintenance costs for woodland are the lowest of all the land uses studied. The low level of maintenance required by most woodland schemes is very important, because all too often reclamation fails to live up to its promise through unwillingness or inability to commit time, staff and money to aftercare. Of all the soft end-uses, woodland is probably the most sensible choice if maintenance budgets are low. However, some maintenance will be needed in all woodland schemes (see Chapter 6).

Legislative background

Before the Second World War, the State had little control over the location of mineral extraction. Many quarries and opencast sites were opened up, but few were restored, and mineral sites became a large element in the body of derelict land. The Midlands ironstone industry was particularly active as the UK depended on native supplies of iron-ore during the war. Nearly 1500 ha of hill and dale topography became derelict as a result, chiefly in

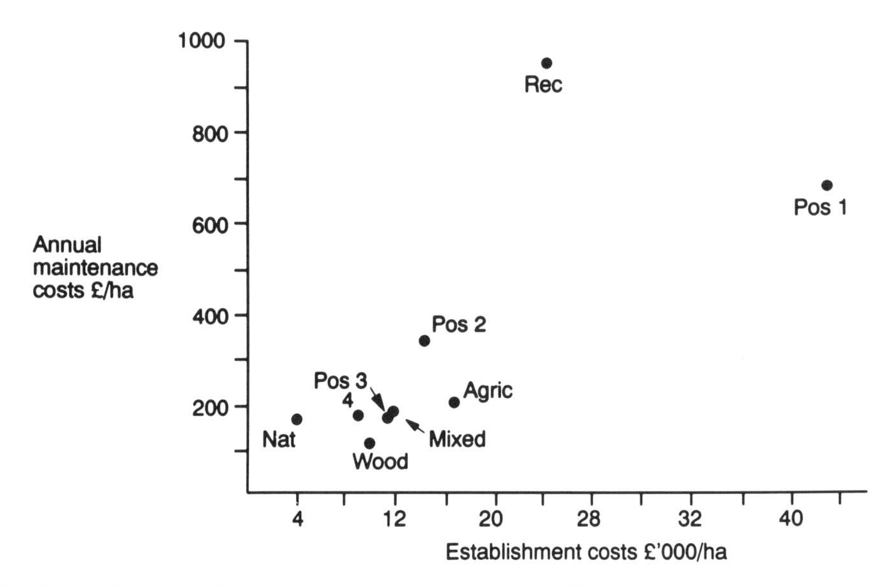

Figure 1.3 Establishment and maintenance costs for a variety of land-uses (from Land Capability Consultants, 1989).

Northamptonshire. A number of parliamentary committees evaluated the need for restoration in the ironstone industry; there followed the Mineral Workings Act (1951), which obliged mineral operators to restore ironstone workings.

Extraction of coal by opencast methods had also begun in 1942 as a wartime emergency measure under the Defence (General) Regulations (1939) to boost the production of indigenous coal supplies. However, after the war, the legacy of unrestored sites was an obviously unwelcome by-product of the opencast mining process. Planned restoration of opencast coal sites began in 1951 following the Opencast Coal Act (1951), succeeded by the Opencast Coal Act (1958). In many parts of the country, dereliction was increased by the large number of colliery spoil heaps produced by deep mining. In 1978, there were still 291 tips in South Wales, representing over 25% of all coal tips in the UK (Commission on Energy and the Environment, 1981). In England, coal tips occupied more than 7500 ha in 1974.

Since the 1960s, several pieces of legislation have been enacted to reduce the total amount of wasteland by encouraging restoration. These include the Local Government Act (1966), the Welsh Development Agency Act (1977), and the Derelict Land Act (1982). The last made grants available for the reclamation of land which is derelict, neglected or unsightly.

The main preventive legislation designed to limit further dereliction following mineral extraction was the Town and Country (Minerals) Act (1981). It was preceded by the Town and Country Planning Act (1971) which formed early control of mineral development. The 1981 Act defined 'mineral planning authorities' and gave them powers to control the environmental effects of mineral workings. The Act also gave new powers to impose **restoration** and **aftercare** conditions (Department of the Environment, 1989) (see Chapters 5 and 6). These powers have been subsumed into the Town and Country Planning Act (1990).

The reclamation of surface mineral workings increasingly involves the filling with waste materials of voids left by mineral extraction. Legislative controls differ according to whether fill materials are mine and quarry wastes, or are household, industrial or commercial wastes. Landfilling with these last three types of 'controlled' waste requires a waste disposal licence under the Waste Management Licensing Regulations (forthcoming). Further controls on the disposal of waste materials on land, including the landfilling of mineral voids, are contained in the Town and Country Planning Act (1990), the Environmental Protection Act (1990) and the Planning and Compensation Act (1991). The latter requires that land used for waste disposal be brought into a state fit for a specified after-use such as agriculture or forestry.

Forestry and the minerals industry

In many regions of Great Britain, the history of forestry, and of the Forestry Commission, is inextricably bound up with that of the minerals industry. Many of the ancient hunting forests are situated in areas which have also been highly regarded for their mineral wealth. For example, both iron-ore and coal have been extracted in the Forest of Dean since Roman times, the former industry finishing around 1900, but coal mining continuing to the present day. Considerable demands were made on the Forest for the production of charcoal, used in the smelting of iron-ores (Hart, 1966). The iron industry also flourished in the Weald where the industry dates back 2000 years, and again benefited from ample supplies of wood for charcoal production. And an important proportion of iron-ore workings in the Midlands have been planted with trees since the 1940s (Newton, 1951).

In more recent times, the sand and gravel industry has been active in areas where forestry is important. This is especially so in areas covered by plateau gravels in southern England where the Forestry Commission established coniferous woodland on comparatively poor soils after the First World War.

One example is Bramshill Forest, where sand and gravel have been extracted from forested areas from the 1970s through to today, with restoration to forestry after mineral extraction.

Deep-mined coal operations have traditionally depended on timber pit props, and it is appropriate that in many parts of the UK restored colliery spoil tips have been planted with trees. In South Wales, there has been a tradition of tree planting on colliery tips dating from before the Second World War. The Forestry Commission has also been heavily involved in woodland establishment on restored opencast coal sites in Wales since 1958 (Broad, 1979). This is mainly because much of the land sought for opencast mining has had a total or partial forest cover, and because historically it has been difficult to restore to other after-uses.

Forestry Commission reclamation research

As well as being directly involved in the planting of trees on disturbed man-made sites, the Forestry Commission has been active in surveying the performance of such plantations, and in research to improve methods of establishing and growing trees on such land.

Early work was confined to assessing existing plantations on ironstone workings (Pinchin, 1951), colliery spoils (Pinchin, 1953; Wood and Thurgood, 1955) and opencast coal spoils (White, 1959). Species trials took place on a number of substrates including sand and gravel workings (Wood *et al.*, 1961), pulverised fuel ash (Neustein and Jobling, 1965) and coal shales (Neustein *et al.*, 1968; Neustein and Jobling, 1969). Formal experimentation into the modification of site conditions began in earnest in the 1970s, with cultivation and fertiliser experiments on sand and gravel workings (Jobling, 1972, 1973; Binns and Fourt, 1976) and on opencast coal spoil (Broad, 1979).

The research momentum grew in the late seventies and eighties with studies commissioned by government agencies. In 1976, the Department of the Environment commissioned a review of the reclamation of colliery spoil heaps with special reference to the establishment of trees on regraded materials (Jobling, 1977). A similar review of restored opencast coal sites was conducted for the National Coal Board Opencast Executive (Jobling, 1978). Further Department of the Environment sponsored research included a study of tree root development in relation to the physical and chemical properties of colliery spoils (Jobling, 1979), and silvicultural research on the improvement of tree establishment and growth on these materials (Jobling and Varcoe, 1985). Another study for the Department of the Environment reviewed the existing state of knowledge about the reclamation of surface mineral workings to forestry, to provide guidance for central and local government and the minerals industry (Wilson, 1985).

Experimental work included the development and testing of the winged tine (Fourt, 1978), the 30 m ridge and furrow landform (Fourt and Carnell, 1979) and the testing of nitrogen-fixing plants (Fourt, 1980a; Fourt and Best, 1981, 1982). Investigations into methods of soil placement were begun (e.g. Fourt, 1984a), and research on the use of sewage sludge on reclamation sites started (e.g. Taylor, 1987; Moffat and Roberts, 1989a). Research continues in a number of these directions.

Since the mid 1980s, important new areas of research have included a detailed study of site factors affecting tree growth on opencast coal spoil (for British Coal Opencast), and an evaluation of the potential for woodland establishment on landfill sites (for the Department of the Environment).

This Bulletin draws together the results of this substantial research programme and the fund of experience gathered over some 40 years. Reclamation of disturbed land will remain a priority, and forestry one very important option.

Chapter 2

Challenges associated with disturbed land

Introduction

Industrial and mineral extraction activities inevitably affect the capability of the sites concerned to support vegetation, including trees. In almost all cases, land so affected is the poorer for it. It is important that people engaged in planning or implementing tree planting schemes on man-made sites are aware of the special features that these kinds of sites may possess. Not all will be immediately obvious from a visual assessment, and some exploratory work may be needed to complement on-site observations (see Chapter 3). Here we discuss the site properties particularly relevant to tree establishment and growth. Ways of dealing with hostile site conditions are discussed in detail in further chapters.

Soil physical properties

Compared with undisturbed soil under long-established woodland, soils on man-made sites are almost always structurally poorer. This is because of disturbance and movement, or because the soil has suffered heavy loads from machinery or traffic. Soil materials may have other undesirable properties such as extremes of texture or stoniness. Soil texture, stone content and structure all influence the ability of trees to root effectively and abstract moisture and nutrients.

Soil texture

This term describes the balance of soil particles of different sizes – the particle size distribution – and is perhaps the most fundamental of all soil physical properties. It is unaffected by soil management, but has a very important influence on the way the soil can, or should, be managed. The range of soil particle sizes is usually divided into three: **sand, silt** and **clay.** In the UK, these are usually defined as sand: 60–2000 µm; silt: 2 µm–60 µm and clay: <2 µm. Almost all British soils are composed of a mixture of these three types of particle, **loams** typifying soils which are well balanced, **sandy** soils predominantly composed of sand-sized particles, and **clayey** soils mainly formed from clay-sized particles.

The soil texture has an indirect influence on most other soil physical properties, especially soil aeration and water-holding capacity.

Soil stoniness

Stones are defined as material larger than 2mm in diameter. Most natural soils contain some stones, but man-made sites may contain stone-sized material of a somewhat different nature and quantity. For example, land affected by building demolition may contain brick, concrete and mortar; sand and gravel workings often possess soils which are particularly stony. Extremely stony substrates may hinder or prevent tree planting, and subsequent tree rooting and stability (Cutler, 1991). Soils containing stones of boulder size will present difficulties for cultivation equipment. In addition, many common stone types such as flint or quartzite affect the water holding capacity of the soil, even when present in comparatively small amounts – such stones reduce the overall soil volume available to hold moisture for plant uptake. This effect is important, and soil stoniness should always be taken into account when deciding the thickness of soil materials needed for sustained tree growth on man-made sites (see Chapter 5).

Soil structure

This term refers to the arrangement of the solid particles in the soil. Most soils are arranged into structural units separated by pores, cracks and fissures. The degree of structural arrangement affects the porosity of the soil, and its water-holding capacity. Under natural conditions, soil structure can take decades or centuries to develop. However, disturbance by man can quickly and drastically affect soil structure, usually detrimentally.

Most soils affected by dereliction or mineral extraction will be more compact than before disturbance. In other words, the soil will have suffered a reduction in its porosity. Compaction is usually caused by surface loading. While still in place, soils are often subject to heavy machinery traffic. Heavy wheeled box scrapers are particularly effective in compacting soil materials (see Plate 10), and can exert static pressure on the soil of 2–3 kg cm^{-2} (Downing, 1977). In addition, shear stresses are generated by the moving tyre or tread, and can have a compacting effect equivalent to more than doubling the static load (Greacen and Sands, 1980). Scrapers exert much higher ground pressures than tracked vehicles, and also damage soils through smearing during wheel slip.

Soil stripping and storage also lead to some soil compaction. Soil stacks 4–5 m high are common on modern mineral sites. These are often constructed using box scrapers and bulldozers, and stacks are deliberately driven on to stabilize them. Added to this, the weight of the soil itself leads to compaction increasing with depth into the stack. The act of replacing soil materials at restoration can also cause compaction (see Chapter 5). Compaction leads to changes in the physical nature of the soil in five important ways:

- restriction of root penetration
- reduction in pore space
- reduction in water holding capacity
- reduction in aeration
- reduction in rates of water movement and gas exchange.

In addition, compaction may also affect the chemical and biological behaviour of the soil (p. 16).

Trees need to root effectively into the soil to abstract moisture and nutrients, and for stability. Reduced above-ground growth is likely if soil compaction restricts root growth. Figure 2.1 shows clearly the effect of increasing compaction on root growth in three species; root penetration is rapidly reduced as soil compaction increases.

Compaction has the effect of reducing the total pore space, making a soil more massive. Large voids especially are removed during compaction, resulting in the reduction of **available water** (water held against gravity and available for plant uptake during the growing season) (Figure 2.2). Compacted soils are generally more droughty, and 'dry up' more quickly than uncompacted ones in the summer.

Compact soils usually suffer more severely from drainage problems in winter months, because their system of draining pores and fissures is lost. Zones of compaction within the disturbed soil profile can lead to perched water tables which cause waterlogging in the soil above. This in turn affects root health and growth, and other biological activity.

Another consequence of compaction is a reduction in the ability of the soil to absorb water after rainfall. This hinders the recharge of the soil's moisture supply in the wetter winter months. As a consequence, surface run-off is promoted and risk of water erosion increased. Erosion of compacted soil stacks is a good example of this phenomenon, leading to the loss of valuable soil material needed for respreading after mineral extraction.

Lack of topsoil

One of the most critical problems associated with derelict and mineral sites is the shortage, or complete lack, of topsoil materials for

Plates 1–4 Examples of the result of mineral working:
1. **(right)** Spoil tip resulting from deep mining of coal, Ayrshire;
2. **(below left)** Unrestored brick clay workings;
3. **(below right)** Deep workings for the extraction of fuller's earth;
4. **(bottom)** Opencast workings for coal, Ayrshire.

Plate 5 Natural colonisation of birch (60 years old) on coal spoils at Newtongrange, Scotland.

Plate 6 Satisfactory stand of conifers on restored coal workings, Gwent.

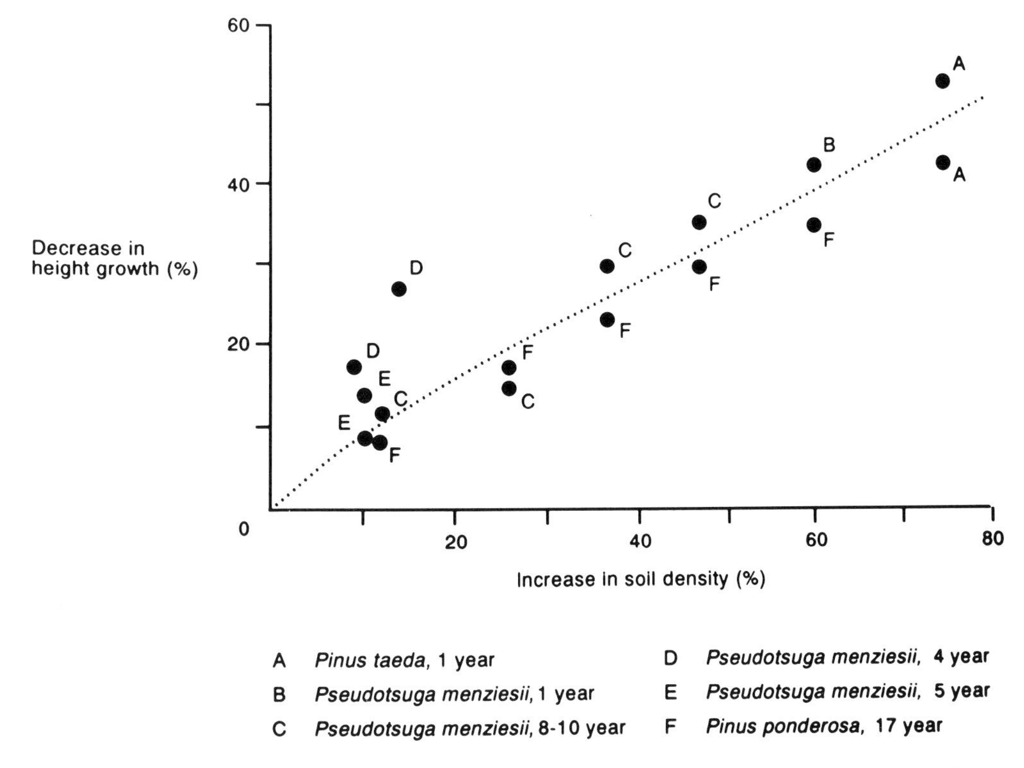

Figure 2.1 Effect of compaction on tree height growth (from Froehlich and McNabb, 1984).

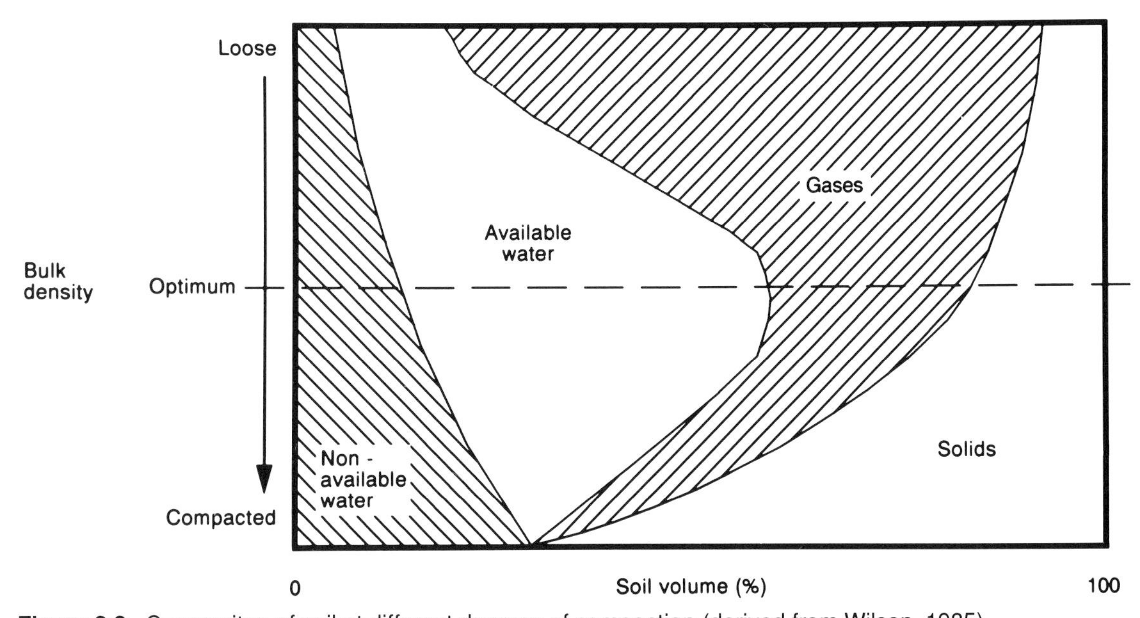

Figure 2.2 Compositon of soil at different degrees of compaction (derived from Wilson, 1985).

restoration. In many cases, tree planting is considered *because* such materials are absent, their absence obviously ruling out other land-uses such as agriculture. Whilst it is true that sites lacking topsoil can be restored to woodland, topsoil should be regarded as a very valuable resource which allows a much greater degree of flexibility in reclamation, especially in the choice of tree species (see Chapter 6).

Sites without topsoil generally suffer from a shortage of nitrogen. This nutrient, above all others, is associated with the organic rich upper soil layers defined as topsoil. Little nitrogen is available in subsoil or overburden materials. Phosphorus, too, may be inadequate for healthy tree growth if topsoil is lacking. The effect of nitrogen and phosphorus deficiency on tree growth can be pronounced. Plate 11 shows an extreme case of nitrogen and phosphorus deficiency in Lodgepole pine on opencast coal overburden in South Wales.

Without topsoil, tree planting must take place in subsoil, or 'soil-forming materials' (see Chapter 3). On mineral sites these may be derived from overburden or rock strata in the mineral excavation. Nutrient supply is very dependent upon the type of material used as soil substitute. Supplies of plant available potassium, magnesium and calcium are usually adequate, but some substrates may lead to an imbalance in nutrient supply. Substrates from ironstone workings are highly susceptible to phosphorus deficiency because phosphorus is strongly bound to the iron minerals in the overburden. Trees planted on alkaline materials such as limestone or chalk waste, or pulverised fuel ash, may suffer from micronutrient deficiencies, especially of iron and manganese. These nutrients are made insoluble in an alkaline environment. Other micronutrient deficiencies are rare, but can occur on certain lithologies.

Other waste materials may cause nutrient toxicities to trees. Pulverised fuel ash is well known for its large boron content, which can severely affect tree growth. In south-west England, levels of micronutrients such as zinc may be very high in metalliferous mining wastes, and associated with other 'heavy metals' (Thornton, 1991) (see Plate 12). Some colliery spoils may become very acidic owing to pyrite oxidation (see Chapter 9), leading to tree death in many instances (see Plate 13). Nutritional problems related to specific types of waste are considered in more detail in Chapter 9.

Hydrological conditions

Man-made sites often suffer from soil waterlogging, arising from several causes. For example, many sand and gravel workings have water-tables relatively close to the land surface. If restoration takes place without the import of fill, the restored land surface will be closer to the watertable than before mineral extraction. In 'low-level' restoration the water table is lowered by permanent pumping, though there are probably no examples in the UK where this form of restoration has taken place with a forestry after-use.

Poor drainage is inherent in sites with a small gradient. These include sand and gravel workings in 'river terrace' gravels, but also many derelict sites such as those adjoining railways or canals. Waterlogging is also a feature of heavy textured (i.e. clayey) substrates, especially in wetter winter months. These materials become wet after rainfall, but are slow to dry out again. The reclamation of brickfield areas is typified by the heavy texture of restoration materials, and their corresponding drainage regime.

Whatever the cause of poor drainage, the effect on tree survival and growth can be marked. Almost all species require an aerated root zone for proper root functioning – only a very few such as poplars and willows can obtain oxygen via the stem (Gill, 1970). Even trees such as alders tend to grow better when in aerated soil (Hook *et al.,* 1987), and their ability to fix nitrogen through the symbiotic relationship with micro-organisms depends upon soil oxygen. Trees intolerant of waterlogged soil conditions show rooting restricted to the aerobic zone in the upper soil layers. If this is shallow, the trees will suffer from summer drought and wind instability. In extreme cases, the trees will die as their summer water demands exceed supply.

Climatic conditions

Most areas of the UK have mineral resources of some kind or other, but some minerals are located in areas which have particularly harsh climatic conditions. For example, china clay spoils in Cornwall can occur at elevations above 300 m OD, where the climate is wet and windy, with rainfall greater than 1200 mm a year (Moffat and Roberts, 1989b). Opencast coal sites in South Wales and south Scotland also experience high rainfall and exposure (see Chapter 9). In contrast, much of the derelict land in Essex and Kent suffers from a relatively dry climate (rainfall <600 mm a year). Most large man-made sites are more exposed than undisturbed ones because hedges, woodland and shelterbelts are usually absent.

Extremes of climate have important consequences for tree establishment and growth. Exposed sites will tend to restrict species choice to the hardiest the site will support, and growth is likely to be comparatively poor. On china clay spoil, Moffat and Roberts (1989b) found a progressive reduction in the mean height of Sitka spruce over a 30 m altitudinal range on an exposed south west facing slope (see Figure 2.3). High rainfall makes soil movement and cultivation difficult to perform in optimum conditions, and makes good drainage design imperative. In contrast, in areas of low rainfall the timing of planting and weed control are critical to avoid drought (see Chapter 6).

Soil contamination

All types of land previously used for industrial purposes are likely to show some signs of contamination, defined here broadly as the introduction of foreign materials to the site. Certain types of site are especially likely to have been contaminated by their past or present use. Examples are chemical works, gasworks, oil refineries, paper and printing works, metal mines, smelters, foundries and metal finishing works (British Standards Institution, 1988), though this list is not exhaustive. Sites adjoining some of these activities may also be affected, such as areas in South Wales downwind of smelting and refining of non-ferrous heavy metals (Goodman and Roberts, 1971).

Of course, the presence of contaminants on a site does not necessarily mean that a hazard exists, either to trees planted on it or to people involved in their planting and maintenance.

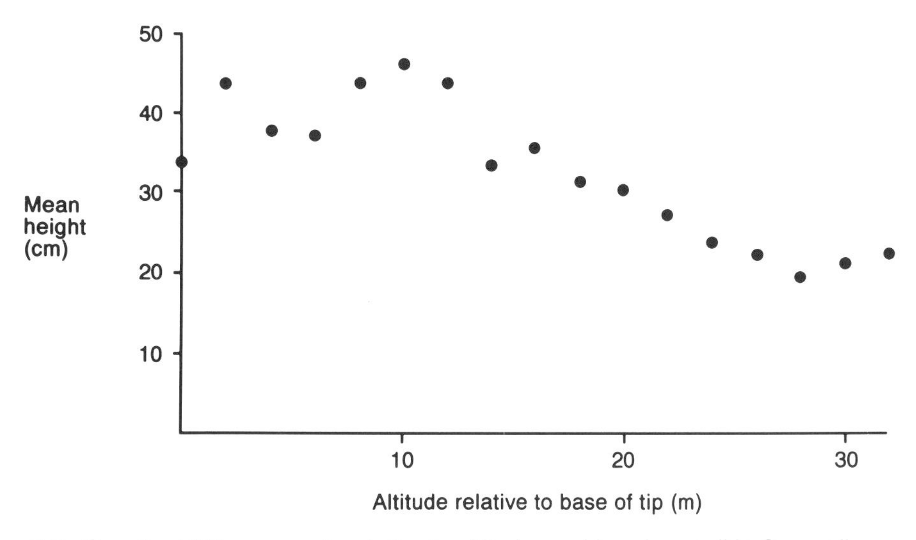

Figure 2.3 Growth of Sitka spruce in relation to altitude on china clay spoil in Cornwall (from Moffat and Roberts, 1989b).

Some substances which pose dangers to human health if they contaminate food materials, may not affect tree growth. Other contaminants such as asbestos can be perfectly acceptable in a tree planting scheme provided that they are buried. However, some contaminants, including some heavy metals, are well known for their adverse effects on vegetation, including trees.

The possibility of serious contamination should always be considered when evaluating a potential site for tree planting. If there is any suggestion that contamination has occurred, then more thorough examination is warranted (see Chapter 7).

Biological activity

The living components of soil, organisms such as earthworms and arthropods or micro-organisms such as bacteria, fungi and algae, are essential in the development and maintenance of the soil ecosystem. The ability of the soil to sustain nutrient supply to plants growing in it depends ultimately on these organisms incorporating organic matter – decomposing and mineralising it into a form suitable for plant uptake. Soil organisms also play an important part in the development and maintenance of soil structure.

Man-made substrates often suffer from a smaller biological population and associated activity than undisturbed soils. Organic matter is a major source of energy for most soil-inhabiting organisms, and substrates lacking organic matter, including most overburden and soil-forming materials, will therefore support only a small biological population. Particular geochemistries may further inhibit biological activity, for example in acidic colliery spoil. Anaerobic conditions caused by waterlogging or compaction will support a different set of organisms from that which occurs in aerobic conditions. By-products of anaerobic bacterial activity include methane, ethane, hydrogen sulphide, nitrous oxides, fatty acids, alcohols and esters. These can harm trees or other plants (Craul, 1985).

Certain types of contamination may restrict the activity of biological organisms. Both soil micro-organisms and invertebrates are affected by heavy metals if present above critical concentrations (Bååth, 1989; Bengtsson and Tranvik, 1989). Organic contaminants such as oils or solvents can also have severe effects on soil biology.

Air pollution

Many man-made sites where tree planting has been attempted, or where future woodland schemes are likely, are near or within urban and industrial development. Many areas of long-standing industry in the UK have suffered from air pollution for decades; one legacy of this pollution is the increased levels of heavy metals in the affected soils. For example, in contaminated areas in South Wales, elevated nickel concentrations in Sitka spruce foliage have been implicated in abnormal tree functioning and growth (Burton *et al.*, 1983). Similarly, emissions of sulphur oxides in the industrial Pennines hindered afforestation in the 1950s (Farrar *et al.*, 1977; Lines, 1979).

Since the Clean Air Acts of 1954 and 1962, emission control has been greater, and modern contamination or pollution from airborne metal sources is rare, though not absent altogether from some point sources. Some industrial areas still experience gaseous air pollution which may affect tree health. For example, fluorides and sulphur dioxide have been identified as harming the growth of trees in the Bedfordshire brickfields (Gilbert, 1983). In general, however, there appears to be little need for concern in most areas where trees may be planted following restoration.

A commonly perceived problem is the effect of dust generated by quarrying operations. In a phased working, dust may affect trees planted in earlier reclaimed phases of the site. Limestone and cement dusts appear to have the most potential to interfere with tree growth (Farmer, 1992), but in other mineral workings the effect of dust on tree health is probably overstated (Roy Waller Associates Ltd, 1991).

Animal damage

Trees planted on reclaimed derelict and mineral sites can suffer browsing or other damage from many different animals; in certain respects, animal pressure may be greater than on more conventional sites. Banks, earthmounds and quarry exposures often form ideal habitats for rabbits. On many infertile sites, with sparse vegetation, the planted tree may offer the only green material and attract animals such as hares, deer and sheep. Alternatively, grass established to stabilize soil mounds may provide useful cover for voles, which then attack trees planted on adjoining land (Hilton, 1967; Radvanyi, 1980). Seagulls are a common problem on sites restored next to landfilling operations, and may pull up newly planted trees (Gawn, 1991). Animal damage, by whatever means, can be severe, and should be anticipated and controlled (see Chapter 6).

Vegetation competition

It is well established that all newly planted trees suffer if there is vigorously growing vegetation around them (Davies, 1987a; Potter, 1989). Sites reclaimed after dereliction or mineral extraction may pose special problems due to the weed species present. Woody legumes such as the tall melilot quickly colonise some newly restored substrates, and can physically smother trees planted there. Coltsfoot is a common coloniser on reclaimed sites, and cansometimes grow luxuriantly, to the detriment of the tree. Natural tree colonisation by seed derived from adjoining areas can also present problems to planned tree establishment. All weeds need controlling early in the life of the newly planted tree (see Chapter 6).

Some forms of weed such as gorse and broom may pose an additional fire risk, especially if the site is located close to urban areas.

Vandalism

Tree planting schemes on man-made sites are prone to vandalism, especially if situated within despoiled or derelict areas where site improvement is conspicuous. Trees cannot be made vandal-proof, though vandalism may be deterred through choice of species, tree stock type, and planting density and design (see Chapter 6).

Section 2 – Reclamation of mineral workings

Chapter 3

Before mineral extraction

Introduction

As discussed in Chapter 1, mineral extraction is now carefully controlled through planning legislation, and the need for both restoration and aftercare has been accepted. However, successful land reclamation is usually very dependent upon its proper consideration well before mineral extraction begins. This Chapter discusses the issues that should be considered. It also covers the statutory role of the Forestry Authority in giving advice to mineral planning and other authorities, and to people who are considering felling woodland before mineral extraction, or reclaiming land to woodland after mineral extraction.

Preparing planning applications – site investigations

The amount and detail of information needed to apply to work a site for minerals is considerable, and includes proposals on how the site will be reclaimed to a beneficial after-use. The kind of information that will enable the mineral planning authorities (and the Forestry Authority as statutory consultees) to judge whether a forestry after-use is practicable is given in the box on the following page, and expanded in Appendix 3.

It is likely that specialised site investigations will be needed to gather some of this information, such as soil resource surveys, surveys of soil-forming materials, and hydrogeological and hydrological surveys.

Soil resource surveys

Soil is the most vital resource for the reclamation of mineral workings. It is therefore important that before mineral extraction takes place, the operator has a good knowledge of the kinds of soil on the site, their location and quantities. Only then can sensible decisions be made about such aspects of the mineral working as choice of machinery to strip and replace soils, soil stack size and height, and the timing of soil moving operations.

Although engineers, foresters and agronomists may differ in their definition of what a soil is, especially in its lower depth, most are agreed that it varies in kind from place to place. Such variation, as for example between sandy and clayey soils, can take place over relatively short distances measured in metres. It is likely that on almost all sites worked for minerals, several contrasting soil types will occur: each will need a different form of management during the restoration process. These different kinds of soil will be characterised, mapped and quantified in amount and extent during a soil resource survey. This practice has been common for many years on land where agricultural restoration has followed mineral extraction, but to date it has been the exception as a precursor to forest reclamation.

Soil surveying can be approached in many different ways, depending on the reasons for performing it, the terrain to be surveyed and the skills of the surveying staff. Most surveying consists of using soil augers and pits to inspect the soil profile in vertical section, and linking these observations to delimit areas of similar soil type. The complexity of the soil pattern will determine the number of observations per unit area. Observations at each site may include soil texture or particle size class,

Details required in a planning application if forestry is proposed as the after-use (from Department of the Environment, 1988)

The nature of the deposit

- The mineral to be extracted.
- The results of any exploration or prospecting work carried out, e.g. boreholes, trial pits etc.
- The nature, thickness and quantities of:
  - topsoil, subsoil and overburden (including reference to soil-forming materials as appropriate)
  - mineral to be extracted
  - waste or non-saleable material.
- The results of tests undertaken to indicate the quality of the deposit, e.g. special physical or chemical properties.
- The geology and topography of the site identifying, where relevant:
  - land stability
  - water table
  - ground conditions, including surface water drainage.

Processing of the materials

- A description of the nature and quantities of processed waste, and the proposed method of disposal.

Restoration, aftercare and after-use

- Intended after-use(s) with appropriate detail on nature and types.
- Contours and intended final levels of the site.
- Use of soil materials in restoration, together with intended phasing and timescale.
- Amounts, types and sources of filling materials if reclamation envisages partial or complete filling with on-site or imported wastes, and the need for any licence under the Environmental Protection Act (1990).
- Details of proposed drainage of the restored land, including creation of any permanent water areas.
- Aftercare proposals – the details will vary according to the intended timescale of restoration and aftercare. Where they will not take place for several years, a summary of the principle items to be included in an aftercare scheme is required.

Plans and drawings

- The proposed levels of the worked out areas.
- The proposed surface area, height and location of mineral stockpiles, and of topsoil, subsoil, and overburden mounds.
- Details of landscaping and restoration including the final levels of the restored site.

colour, organic matter content, structure, root content and horizonation: this information will allow the volume of different soil layers and types to be estimated.

Soil surveying is a skilled job, and is best performed by professional soil consultants. On undisturbed sites, skilled surveyors can assess soil resources using a combination of direct observations (auger borings, soil pits) at sites chosen subjectively, and interpretation using the topography, vegetation and land-use to indicate where soil types change from one to another in the landscape. On disturbed sites or derelict land, interpretation in this way is much more difficult, and soil observation density usually needs to be greater. In contrast to undisturbed sites, a grid survey approach should be adopted, based on regularly spaced, predetermined sampling points. This method ensures that the site is covered equally, and that reliable estimates of proportions of different soil types are obtained. In addition, it is possible to return to the original sampling positions, should further sampling be necessary (e.g. for unforeseen chemical analyses). Methods of soil survey have been reviewed by Avery (1987). Bridges (1987) gives details of how soil survey and sampling on derelict land is best approached.

Because soil physical properties are crucial to the satisfactory stripping, storing and replacing of soil materials, it is these that are focused on in surveys of undisturbed sites. In addition, most physical appraisals can take place in the field. However, chemical properties such as heavy metal contents may be important on sites affected by contamination. More intensive soil sampling may be needed on these sites (see Chapter 7).

Identification of soil-forming materials

On many sites where mineral extraction or other industrial activity has taken place, there is commonly a shortage of soil materials: such materials are often buried, contaminated or otherwise lost. When a soil resource survey reveals that a shortage of soil materials is likely to be a problem at the restoration stage, it is important to identify soil-forming materials, preferably before mineral extraction begins.

Soil-forming materials are those that are capable of forming a substrate for tree growth. They must be satisfactory both physically and chemically; in particular, they should possess an adequate amount of soil-sized particles to promote water supply for plant uptake, and they must not be toxic to plants. In addition, soil-forming materials must be capable of being stripped, stored and replaced: very clayey materials, for example, are unlikely to be suitable for most uses.

It should be emphasised that soil-forming materials are exactly what their name suggests – they are the raw building blocks of a future soil that may take decades or centuries to develop. And because they are likely to be derived from geological materials below the present land surface, they are almost always deficient in some plant nutrients, especially nitrogen. With little or no organic matter, soil structure is usually absent or weakly developed, and the material is liable to slaking and instability. Soil-forming materials may therefore require sensitive aftercare, including careful placement and cultivation, the addition of nutrients as fertiliser, or inclusion of nitrogen-fixing plants and tree species as components of the planting scheme (see Chapter 6).

Soil-forming materials may be found in the overburden overlying the minerals to be extracted. For example, at the Derlwyn opencast coal site in West Glamorgan, weathered shale materials were identified underlying the natural soil derived from clayey glacial till. The latter was considered a material which would be very difficult to move sensitively. It was therefore discarded to be replaced by the weathered shale as the soil-forming material for the restoration of the site. Geochemical analysis of the weathered shale also revealed it as a more amenable material for tree growth than the clayey till.

Other soil-forming materials may be identified deeper in the geological strata, from either borehole logs or exposures adjoining the potential mineral site. In some locations these materials may provide the only on-site possibilities for a soil cover, and should be clearly identified so that they can be saved during the working of the site. Material from core drilling, taken during the geological exploratory phase, will need laboratory analysis to determine the concentration of nutrients and toxic substances, and its general suitability as a soil substitute. Table 3.1 lists important physical and chemical tests which should be undertaken on sites where soil-forming materials are sought. Suitability criteria will vary from site to site, and will depend on the type of woodland cover intended after restoration, but guidelines are given in Table 3.2.

Borehole logs and tests on core samples will enable soil-forming materials to be identified, but other geophysical techniques may be needed to elucidate the spatial extent of the chosen materials. Volumetric estimates of the materials can then be made, and plans for stripping and storage drawn up.

Daniels and Amos (1984) and Moffat (1987) give some useful guidance on general choice of mining overburden types for use as soil-forming materials (see Table 3.3). Freshly blasted spoils usually range from 30–60% soil-sized (<2 mm) fragments, which will hold adequate amounts of water when present in a sufficient non-compacted thickness. Well blasted and weathered strata lying close to the ground surface tend to shatter, yielding spoils which can be too heavily textured for easy handling. Pure siltstones should be avoided because of their tendency to crust. Mixtures of sandstone and siltstone yield materials with a loamy texture, good water retention and moderately high cation exchange capacity. Ferruginous materials should be avoided because they fix phosphorus, making it unavailable for plant uptake. Limestone can produce soil-forming

Table 3.1 Information needed to assess the acceptability of overburden as soil-forming material

1. Strata thickness
2. Strata persistence
3. Acid–base balance[1]
4. pH
5. Soluble salt content/electrical conductivity
6. Texture
7. Iron pyrite content[1]
8. Heavy metal content[2]
9. Plant available nutrients
10. Cation exchange capacity

[1] particularly in coal spoils
[2] particularly in metalliferous/igneous spoils

Table 3.2 Minimum standards for soil-forming materials used in restoration to forestry

1. Bulk density	<1.5 g cm^{-3} to at least 0.5 m depth <1.7 g cm^{-3} to 1 m depth
2. Stoniness	<40% by volume; few stones greater than 100 mm in size
3. pH	3.5 to 8.5
4. Electrical conductivity	<2000 μScm^{-1} (1:1 soil:water suspension)
5. Iron pyrite content	<0.5%
6. Heavy metal content	Not excessively over ICRCL* threshold trigger concentrations (ICRCL, 1987)
7. Organic contaminants	Not exceeding ICRCL action trigger concentrations (ICRCL, 1987)

* Interdepartmental Committee on the Redevelopment of Contaminated Land

Table 3.3 Mining overburden types and their principal limitations for tree growth

Mining operation	*Type of overburden/soil*	*Texture*[1]	*Major problems for tree establishment*
Opencast coal	Shaly drift, often till; mudstones in Midlands	ZCL, CL and C; some peat	Heavy textures lead to winter waterlogging and summer drought; stoniness; liability to compaction and erosion; N,P deficiencies
Ironstone	Ferritic loam	CL, SL	Droughtiness and erodibility; fixation leading to P deficiency; N deficiency; possible Mg deficiency and low pH
Limestones			
Jurassic	Thin calcareous soils over limestone rock	CL, ZCL, SCL	High pH restricts species choice; soil droughtiness due to stoniness; N deficiency; risk of lime-induced chlorosis
Carboniferous	Drift; till in N. England, silty drift in Midlands; some thinner calcareous soils in S. Wales	Dominantly clayey till; ZCL in Midlands	Heavy textures lead to winter waterlogging and summer drought; liability to compaction; silty drift particularly erodible; N deficiency
Chalk	Thin calcareous soils directly over chalk	ZCL	High pH restricts species choice; N, P, K deficiencies; risk of lime-induced chlorosis
Clay/shales	Till covered in many places	Dominantly clayey, though lighter textured material does occur	Heavy textures lead to winter waterlogging and summer drought; liability to compaction; N deficiency

[1] ZCL silty clay loam, CL clay loam, C clay, SL sandy loam, SCL sandy clay loam

(*continued*)

Table 3.3 Mining overburden types and their principal limitations for tree growth *continued*

Mining operation	*Type of overburden/soil*	*Texture*[1]	*Major problems for tree establishment*
Gravels			
Plateau	Stony, sandy or loamy soil	SL, LS	Droughtiness; stoniness; low pH; N,P deficiencies
River Terrace	Variable	Variable	High groundwater levels; often low pH; other limitations depend on texture and stoniness of soil-forming materials
China clay	Coarse, gritty	S	Pronounced droughtiness; low pH; N, P, K, Mg deficiencies
Igneous	Gritty drift, often with peat surface	SZL, SL	Low pH; P deficiency
Vein minerals	Wastes, variable	Variable	Heavy metal toxicity; N,P deficiencies; drought risk

[1] SL sandy loam, LS loamy sand, S sand, SZL sandy silt loam

materials, but their high pH restricts tree species choice to the few tolerant of alkaline conditions. However, these general guidelines will vary in applicability, depending on the geology to be exploited in the mining process.

Hydrogeological and hydrological surveys

Mining and quarrying inevitably affect the hydrogeological and hydrological conditions of sites and their surroundings. For example, discharge of effluent, removal of filtering strata, or the contamination of surface or rain water by contact with disturbed strata may all lead to pollution of rivers or underground water supplies. The disturbance of land may also interfere with the natural flow of springs (Department of the Environment, 1988). A hydrogeological survey assesses the site so that the effects of mining can be predicted and accommodated in any planning application submitted.

Site hydrology after restoration is also likely to be substantially changed from original conditions. For example, restoration with imported fill will affect water movement across the site. The choice of surface materials, their emplacement and subsequent cultivation will affect the degree of surface run-off, itself controlled by drainage and design. On many restored opencast coal sites, for example, peak outfall flow is frequently substantially higher than might have been expected, and the time-lapse between peak rainfall and peak flow is short (Kemp, 1988).

The success of a forestry reclamation scheme may depend directly on the ability to predict and control site hydrology and hydrogeology. For example, it is important that the water-table in the restored landform is below the desired depth of tree rooting. But a forestry reclamation project will also be judged on its effect on the water quality and stream hydrograph, for example if suspended solids are above permitted levels, or outfall hydrographs very peaked in nature. Sensible landform and drainage design can help to alleviate the inevitable effects on the hydrology of a site caused by mining operations (see Chapter 5).

The role of the Forestry Authority

The Forestry Authority should be consulted if any of the following apply:

- if woodland on the land proposed for mineral working is dedicated under the Forestry Commission Dedication Scheme, or grant-aided under Section 1 of the Forestry Act (1979)

- if it is proposed that the land be reclaimed for a forestry after-use
- if tree planting is to be supported by a grant under the Woodland Grant Scheme or Community Woodland Supplement.

Felling of woodland subject to a Forestry Commission Dedication Scheme Agreement

This Scheme was introduced in 1947, and was designed to ensure that forestry formed part of an effective pattern of rural land use, in which it would harmonise to the best possible advantage with agriculture and the environment. Under the Scheme, woodland owners received an outright payment per hectare when approved planting took place. In return, they were obliged (usually by Deed or Agreement of Covenant) to manage woodlands within the scheme in accordance with Plans of Operations.

Under the first two versions of the Dedication Scheme (Basis I and Basis II), the land owners and their successors in title were obliged to use the land solely for forestry purposes. Only with the prior consent of the Forestry Commission could forestry use be waived for other purposes such as mineral extraction. However, it is now the Forestry Authority's policy to phase out Dedication, and obligations under the Basis I and II agreements will normally be terminated on application to the Forestry Authority. Basis III agreements normally come to an end when approved felling takes place.

Felling of trees subject to the conditions of a Forestry Authority grant

The felling of trees planted under one of the Forestry Authority's grant schemes should only take place in accordance with an approved plan of operations. If it does not, the Forestry Authority may have the right to seek reimbursement of grant paid (Forestry Commission, 1991a).

The Forestry Authority in the mineral planning process

Since the passing of the Town and Country Planning (Minerals) Act (1981) (now incorporated in the Town and Country Planning Act (1990)), there is a statutory requirement for mineral planning authorities to consult the Forestry Authority before imposing an aftercare condition on a mineral developer who wishes to reclaim the land for forestry. The Forestry Authority must also examine the terms of an aftercare scheme before they can be approved. There is no statutory requirement, however, for the mineral planning authority to consult the Forestry Authority about the restoration conditions they may wish to impose. This contrasts with agriculture, where the mineral planning authority must consult the Ministry of Agriculture, Fisheries and Food (MAFF) about restoration as well as aftercare. However, Department of the Environment guidance in the Minerals Planning Guidance Note 7 (MPG7) (Department of the Environment, 1989) makes it clear that, in a forestry context, the achievement of good standards during aftercare is very dependent on satisfactory restoration. For example, in many reclamation schemes where forestry is the proposed after-use, the replacement of adequate soil materials is rare, and new soil-forming materials must be sought. However, these cannot be chosen without regard to their mechanical, hydrological and nutritional characteristics – properties which directly impinge upon most aftercare procedures. MPG7 therefore recommends that mineral planning authorities seek advice from the Forestry Authority on all planning conditions which are likely to affect the ultimate success of forestry aftercare (Department of the Environment, 1989).

In response to the statutory requirement to give advice, the Forestry Commission has officers in all its regions who liaise with mineral planning authorities where forestry is the proposed after-use. Appendix 4 lists the offices where this expertise can be sought.

Chapter 4
During mineral extraction

Introduction

In this Chapter, important operations, which take place during mineral extraction but affect the success of the final reclamation of the site, are described. Techniques that minimise the level of disturbance and damage to the site resources are emphasized.

Tree felling

In the past, most mineral-working areas returned to a forestry after-use on reclamation were under woodland before mineral extraction began. The South Wales coal measures and the southern England plateau gravels are good examples of where a forestry–mineral extraction–forestry sequence of events has occurred (Moffat, 1987). Potential mineral sites under forest present the mineral operator with more activities than a site currently used for agriculture: the trees must be felled and all tree parts removed sensitively from the working area of the site before soil stripping can begin. Planning and proper execution of these operations are essential to the longer term aim of good reclamation practice. In addition, there may be both physical and economic constraints on normal felling practice for the forestry contractors who perform this work.

On large mineral sites, such as many of the modern opencast coal workings, a phased operation is usual, with only part of the site being worked at any one time. It is sensible to plan felling in line with the phasing of mineral working, to allow the trees on the later stages of the working to grow and accrue volume for longer. These trees will also be valuable as screens for the working, with the added benefits of noise and dust attenuation (Cook and Van Haverbeke, 1972). Phased felling will also help to balance the needs of the mineral operator with the demands of the timber market; large and sudden felling on the orders of the mineral operator may lead to local market saturation, and little or no return for the produce.

There may be additional costs associated with the tree felling. Planning conditions on the working of the mineral site may include permitted times of working, which may restrict both felling and harvesting operations and the movement of timber lorries. The area of felling will be determined not primarily for silvicultural reasons, but on the requirements for site operation. Access to the area to be felled may be poor, and new roads may need to be made. It may be necessary to ensure that all vehicles associated with the felling are washed free from soil and overburden if they have to travel over particularly adhesive materials – vehicle washing is often a condition of a planning permission to work a site for minerals.

Tree felling and harvesting operations can seriously affect the ultimate success of reclamation, through their impact on soil conditions. Large machinery is now used in these processes: for example, forwarders can extract up to 18 tonnes of timber and weigh over 35 tonnes fully loaded. Ground static pressures of over 100 kPa may be exerted, but shear stress generated by the moving tyre or track may have a compaction effect equivalent to more than double the static load (Greacen and Sands, 1980). Harvesting in wet conditions, especially during the winter, is most likely to cause soil compaction because wet soil is weak and least able to withstand the pressure that the harvesting machinery exerts. If possible, therefore, it is important to plan harvesting for the drier times of the year, minimising soil compaction. Harvesting from pre-planned designated routes through the clearfelled area is probably the best option for preventing widespread compaction damage (Froehlich and McNabb, 1984). The Forestry Commission *Forests and water guidelines* (Forestry Commission, 1993) should always be followed during harvesting operations.

To date, few mineral workings have involved the need to fell areas of broadleaved woodland. Probably the best time to do this is in the autumn, after leaf fall but before winter rains soften up the soil. The nutrient value of the leaf litter can be considerable, and it is important to save this material along with the topsoil which will be stripped and stored.

Removal of harvesting residues

Harvesting residues include lop and top, and tree stumps and roots. They are composed predominantly of woody material, and have little nutritional value unless chipped and composted. Lop and top may be placed in heaps or windrows for burning or eventual burial in the mineral void. A 360° excavator fitted with power forks is suitable for this purpose; dozing should be avoided as experience shows that on ploughed ground much of the debris falls into the furrows and is therefore difficult to collect.

Local circumstances will determine whether burning is environmentally acceptable – a planning condition may require burial. If burning is allowed, it should be undertaken, if at all possible, outside of any fire hazard season (usually spring) and when surrounding vegetation is wet.

There is now considerable interest in ways of utilising harvesting residues (Selmes, 1992). Chipped residues can be marketed for their energy value, or composted to produce a valuable horticultural product or soil improver. Research on the last use is currently being carried out on restored opencast coal spoils in South Wales.

If soils are to be stripped and stored for replacement at the time of restoration, it is important that tree stumps and roots are removed as cleanly as possible. Stumps should be dug out with an excavator: if soil adheres to them, it should be shaken free, or allowed to dry when further disturbance will generally promote its separation from the tree roots. Bulldozers are generally unacceptable in destumping a site – they cannot separate soil and root material cleanly and are liable to compact the soil unless a low ground pressure type of plant is used. It is difficult to burn stumps and roots satisfactorily unless ignition is promoted with the addition of more flammable materials, for example redundant plant tyres. More often it will be appropriate to bury these materials in the mineral void.

Conditions on the timing of harvesting operations also apply to destumping – on no account should this take place in wet weather, or when soil conditions are wet. In both operations, low ground pressure equipment should be employed; it should travel over harvesting debris wherever possible to minimize adverse effects on the soil. Trafficking should be kept to a minimum.

Soil stripping

Successful reclamation will depend to a large extent on the ability of the mineral operator to identify soil resources on site (see Chapter 3), and then to strip them for saving during, and replacement after, mineral extraction. Considerable damage can occur during the stripping operation, and compaction and smearing usually accompany it: it is very important that these effects are minimized. In addition, careless soil stripping can cause dilution of valuable topsoil by subsoil and overburden materials, or soil materials can be lost altogether.

Soil resource mapping should provide the site engineer with details of where different soil types are, how thick they are, and their important physical properties. This information should be used in the planning of the sequence of stripping operations. Different or

Plate 7 (top) Wetland features built into the reclamation of the Woorgreen opencast coal workings, Forest of Dean.

Plate 8 (above) Dunraven Lake, restored opencast coal workings, West Glamorgan.

Plate 9 Argoed Country Park, reclaimed after working for coal.

Plate 10 Widespread trafficking by earthscrapers, leading to soil compaction.

Plate 11 (top, right) Nitrogen and phosphorus deficient lodgepole pine on restored opencast coal spoils in West Glamorgan.

Plate 12 (above , left) Monterey pine (*Pinus radiata*) on heavy metal contaminated spoils in Cornwall.

Plate 13 (above, right) Death of ground vegetation and newly planted trees on pyritic colliery spoil, Mid Glamorgan.

Plate 14 (left) Soil stripping using excavator and dumptruck.

contrasting soil materials should be stripped and stored separately (Department of the Environment, 1989). Most mineral planning authorities will stipulate this as a condition of the planning permission. Soil damage can be minimised by restricting the stripping operation to times when the soil is most likely to be dry, for example late spring and summer. Many mineral planning authorities also stipulate a friable soil condition, and put an embargo on stripping in wet weather or before a set time after rainfall has ceased. Unfortunately, there is no universal procedure for deciding when stripping is safe. Differences in topsoil- and subsoil-handling characteristics suggest that a single set of rainfall criteria may be inadequate (Ramsay, 1986). It is important, therefore, that suitability is judged by observation of the soil itself – reliance on predicted behaviour after rainfall may lead to bad practice.

Damage can also be caused during the stripping operations by unnecessary movement of machinery and plant over unstripped soils. This must be minimised by confining the movement of vehicles to pre-planned routeways.

Damage to soils can be reduced by the direct respreading of stripped soils in progressive or phased restoration (Department of the Environment, 1989). Storage in soil stacks, with consequent deterioration in soil quality, is avoided, and double handling eliminated.

Table 4.1 lists equipment available for bulk soil handling; a wide variety of machines is currently used. Although the Department of the Environment Minerals Planning Guidance Note 7 (1989) states that it is rare for particular types of equipment to be specified in planning conditions, it is increasingly recognised that earthscrapers probably cause the most damage to soils; in contrast, soil removed by excavator (backactor) and dumptruck usually suffers little compaction (Department of the Environment, 1986) (see Plate 14). For a forestry after-use, it is extremely important that compaction is minimised (Chapter 2), and the backactor and dumptruck method is the preferred means of soil lifting.

Table 4.1 Equipment for bulk soil-handling (from Ramsay, 1986)

Lifting	*Transport*	*Placement*
Bulldozer	Bulldozer	Bulldozer
Front loader	Dump truck	Light bulldozer or back-acting shovel[1] (Front loader to Front shovel)
Face shovel	Dump truck	
Bucket wheel excavator	Conveyor belt	
Dragline bucket	Dump truck	
Back-acting shovel	Dump truck	
Front shovel	Dump truck	
Earthscraper	Earthscraper	Earthscraper/ back-acting shovel[2]

[1] Prefered methods
[2] Least preferred method

Soils should be lifted not only from areas where minerals are to be worked, but also from any areas to be used for roads, buildings, plant, lagoons or soil and overburden mounds.

Peat, or other soils with a thick organic-rich topsoil, often occur beneath forests under which minerals are sought, especially coal to be won by opencast methods (e.g. Fourt, 1984b). With care, these materials can be treated in the same way as topsoil, and lifted, stored and replaced to form a medium for tree planting (Moffat, 1987). Compared with tree growth on mineral spoil, growth on restored peat is considerably and significantly better (see Table 4.2) (McNeill and Moffat, 1992). This suggests that, wherever possible, peaty materials should be identified in soil resource surveys, and stripped and saved for replacement. Special care must be taken to store peat safely and effectively: its stability can be impaired if it is allowed to absorb too much water and this will reduce its value as a soil material when respread. In addition, the quality of water draining from peat stores should be monitored, and anti-pollution control measures considered.

Soil storage

Much recent research shows that soil storage inevitably affects deleteriously the quality of the soil. Soils in stockpiles are more compact, poorer in organic matter, and altered chemi-

Table 4.2 Height and height increment of Sitka spruce on opencast coal spoil compared with peat (from McNeill and Moffat, 1992)

	Height (cm)				*Increment (cm)*	
	At planting		*5 years*		*5 years*	
Treatments	*Peat*	*Mineral*	*Peat*	*Mineral*	*Peat*	*Mineral*
No nitrogen	39.0	39.9	164.1	89.2	125.1	49.3
Legume sown	38.7	37.5	163.6	105.4	124.9	67.9
Legume + phosphate	36.5	38.3	170.1	104.1	133.6	65.8
Interplanted alder	35.3	38.3	152.1	114.3	116.8	76.0
Biennial urea	37.7	43.8	163.3	112.8	125.6	69.0
Periodic urea	35.4	38.5	164.1	97.9	128.7	59.4
Mean	37.1	39.4	162.9	103.9	125.8	64.6

cally, biologically and microbiologically (Scullion *et al.*, 1988; Harris *et al.*, 1989; Williamson and Johnson, 1990). These changes can take place very rapidly after storage (Rimmer, 1991). Their magnitude can be minimised by constructing low, wide mounds rather than tall and narrow ones (Department of the Environment, 1986). However, for many sites, there is little room to accommodate mounds lower than 5–6 m in height, though it should be appreciated that this size is larger than ideal. They should be set well back from any future position of the mineral void to prevent soil loss into it. Mounds should be designed to shed water, and the top should always have a cross slope of at least 1 in 50 (1°) (Bransden, 1991). It may be necessary to compact stored materials so that rainfall ingress is hindered, though the procedure should be kept to the minimum necessary to accomplish the aim.

Most planning conditions stipulate that mounds be seeded and grassed. Deep rooting species are preferred so that the maximum thickness of the mound may remain aerobic. Fertilisers may be necessary to encourage good growth on more infertile subsoil or soil-forming material stores. Weeds will require control using chemical herbicides. Once formed, mounds should not be traversed by any machinery until the soil is to be replaced after mineral extraction.

Chapter 5

Restoration

Introduction

Under the Town and Country Planning Act (1990), reclamation is treated as a two phase operation once mineral extraction has ceased. It includes both restoration and aftercare (Chapter 1). Department of the Environment Minerals Planning Guidance Note 7 describes **restoration** as the replacement of any, or all, topsoil, subsoil and soil-forming materials. **Aftercare** is any or all of the operations of 'planting, cultivating, fertilising, watering, draining or otherwise treating the land' for a specified end-use after restoration has finished (Department of the Environment, 1989). Restoration implies that the form of the land has been determined and prepared ready for soil replacement – in other words restoration leaves the land at its final contour. Aftercare will not drastically change the restored landform shape or appearance.

As discussed in Chapter 3, in forestry the restoration phase is crucial to the success of the whole reclamation scheme. For example, underdrainage, an aftercare operation in agricultural reclamation, is rarely considered in forestry, and most opportunities to produce a well drained site occur during the restoration stage, when landforming takes place. In fact, the soil water regime is one of the most critical site properties to consider if forestry reclamation is to be successful – if opportunities are missed during restoration, it will usually be impossible to remedy later on. In addition, a waterlogged site has deleterious indirect effects on cultivating, fertilising and planting operations, as well as direct effects on tree growth (Chapter 2).

Hence, the distinction in definition between restoration and aftercare is somewhat artificial in the forestry context. And there are large risks to successful reclamation if aftercare and restoration are considered as sequential and separate operations, and little thought given to aftercare before restoration is completed (Moffat, 1987; Department of the Environment, 1989).

Notwithstanding this argument, the restoration phase *is* the first step in reclamation after mineral extraction. This Chapter deals with important aspects of the restoration phase for woodland establishment and aftercare, particularly the design of the restored land surface and soil replacement. In addition, Appendix 5 gives a specimen set of reclamation conditions for planning permission where forestry is the proposed after-use. Although the Chapter is composed in the context of mineral reclamation, much will be relevant to the restoration of derelict land and landfill sites.

Landform

Design of the final landform is a task which may involve a number of disciplines, including silviculture, engineering and landscape architecture. Each will have standards that it wishes to impose on the design, and it is important that each understands the needs of the other so that the final design satisfies, as far as possible, all parties. The following site properties are influenced or controlled by landform design, and are discussed in some detail.

Drainage

On all mineral sites, attention should be paid to the effect the restored landform has on the volume and nature of water to be discharged to receiving off-site watercourses. Factors which affect surface water run-off include:

- the nature of the drainage network on the restored site
- the nature of materials used at the restored landform surface
- the degree of compaction of the surface layer(s)
- the nature and extent of cultivation
- the extent of a vegetation cover
- the landform shape and gradient
- changes in ground water movement.

The surface drainage network is the most important feature in the control of water discharge to receiving watercourses. Simplistically, the greater the time it takes for rain falling on the most distant part of a catchment to reach the site outfall, the greater is the protection afforded to the off-site watercourse. Engineering design should aim to slow down or temporarily hold water on-site in order to control the surface water discharge. This can be achieved in number of ways.

1 On long slopes, 'contour berms' (p. 34) are recommended to limit the down slope movement of surface water which, if not controlled, can cause severe scouring of the restored land surface. In addition, berms serve to lengthen the distance the surface water has to travel to reach the site outfall.

2 On many sites it is necessary for the on-site watercourses to exceed the gradient where scouring is unlikely to occur (c. 1° to 2°). Where steeper gradients are necessary, durable stone armouring should be constructed along the channel bed and sides. Stone armouring is preferable to concrete-lined channels because it is flexible and allows for the settlement of underlying overburden. It also provides a rough surface which dissipates water energy, slows down water flow and increases the time for water to reach the site outfall. In addition, stone channels fit more comfortably in a rural setting.

3 As described in other chapters, soil compaction must be prevented or relieved to provide the best opportunity for tree establishment. There is also a possible benefit to drainage if the restored surface is loose, friable and uncompacted because this allows the downward percolation of water as well as increasing water holding capacity within the soil profile itself. If the restored surface is compact, rain falling on the site is quickly shed and concentrates rapidly at the site outfalls. Cultivation (p. 42) is recommended if compaction is present in the upper soil layers.

4 Water features such as ponds or lakes built into the newly restored site (p. 36) can be used to control surface water flows. Most wetland features are capable of withstanding periodic increases in water level without detriment to the facilities they provide. The increase in water level can greatly assist in limiting the volume of water that reaches the site outfall at any one time. The control of the water flow from a wetland feature is usually by means of a pipe which has a capacity to carry less water than may enter the pond during heavy rain. This throttling effect causes the water level to rise, creating a temporary reservoir. As the peak flows into the pond abate, the outfall pipe continues to discharge water at a controlled rate and water levels fall to the level of the outfall pipe.

5 A ground vegetation cover acts physically to slow the flow of water across a reclaimed site. In addition, transpiration may reduce the volume of water that contributes to the site outfall.

Water management is an essential consideration in the reclamation of mineral workings; engineering advice should usually be sought.

Soil water regime

As noted (p. 31), the primary control on the soil water regime is landform design. A considerable amount of evidence suggests that excess water will not be removed effectively from a restored site unless slopes of about 1 in

10 (5½–6°) are provided (Wilson, 1985; Moffat, 1987). In high rainfall areas such as South Wales, tree growth, and especially rooting depth, can suffer as a result of poor soil drainage (Bending *et al.*, 1991).

On many sites, slopes greater than 6° are commonplace; shedding of excess water after rainfall is relatively rapid, and the main concerns are soil erosion and water management (p. 32). However, some minerals such as sand and gravel are mainly derived from flat river terrace and plateau positions (see Chapter 9), where risk of soil waterlogging is greater. In the past, Forestry Commission advice has been to construct ridges with side slopes of c. 6°, so that the maximum area of the site is gently sloping. Large ridges, 30 m across and 1.5 m high were suggested in the 1980s (Fourt and Carnell, 1979; Fourt, 1980b; Binns and Fourt, 1981; Binns, 1982). Two systems were proposed, one suitable for sites where slowly permeable or impermeable materials were used to floor the site, and another for sites where porous materials were present within 0.3 m of the furrow bottom (see Figure 5.1). In the former system, ridges would be cross ripped to a depth of 0.5 m to relieve compaction, and to increase infiltration and lateral flow of water; open drains would be constructed to carry away water issuing from the ridges. In the latter system, ripping would be performed to a depth of 0.75 m, followed by one final pass along the furrow to ensure thorough water percolation.

The ridge and furrow landform has recently been evaluated for its effect on tree growth (Moffat and Roberts, 1989c). The study concluded that this system does succeed in reducing waterlogging over most of the ridge area. In wetter parts of the country, this has promoted tree growth, probably because roots can exploit a greater depth of aerated soil. However, in drier regions, especially in eastern England, the higher parts of the ridge are associated with poorer tree growth because they can suffer long periods of large soil water deficits in summer months. The results of the study support the use of the ridge and furrow landform in areas where rainfall is high and soil moisture deficits are low. However, in

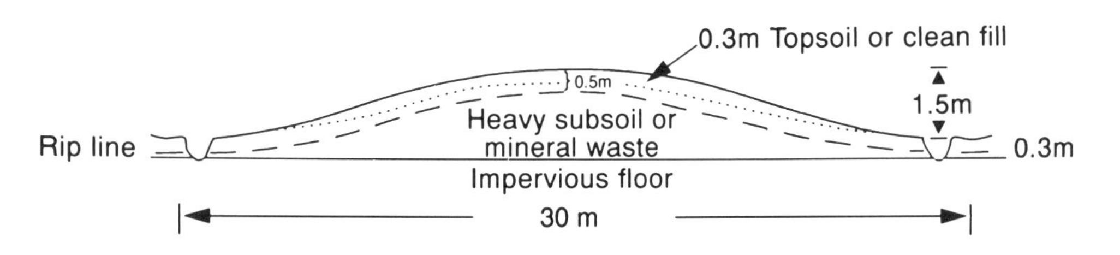

Figure 5.1a

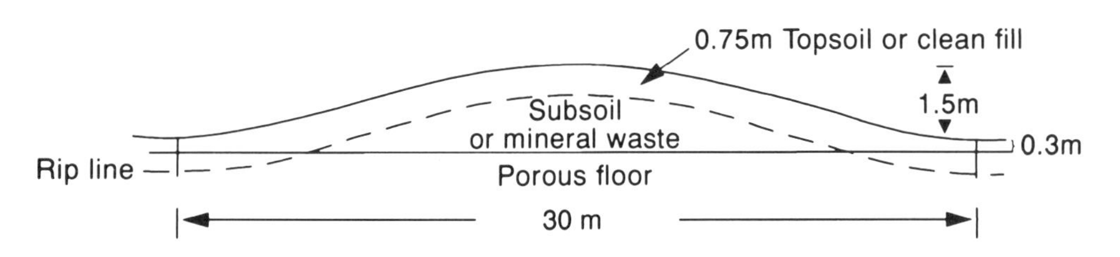

Figure 5.1b

Figure 5.1 Ridge and furrow landforms: a. system suitable for sites with high water-tables; b. system suitable for permeable sites.

drier parts of the country, or where water tables are consistently deep in the soil, the use of the ridge and furrow landform is inappropriate. Moffat and Roberts (1989c) suggested that the ridges in these areas might be reduced in amplitude to reduce the depth to the water table in the summer. Nevertheless, very flat ground should be avoided if at all possible.

Steep slopes can also affect drainage status, with very steep slopes suffering excessive drainage and droughtiness.

Soil erosion

Soil erosion risk is generally higher on sites which have suffered soil movement and replacement; erosion risk is exacerbated by the sparse vegetation cover that often exists on infertile soil or soil-forming materials (see Plate 15). Erosion risk can be reduced by sensible landform design, and heightened considerably by injudicious design. Catchment size, and slope angle, length and shape are probably the most important landform attributes, and on many sites these can be controlled quite carefully.

The relationship between erosion risk and these parameters is complex, but it is clear that risk increases non-linearly with increase in slope angle or length. For example, for colliery spoil Haigh (1979) reported that the increase of erosion in relation to slope angle reaches a peak somewhere between 26° and 45°, depending on the bulk density of the eroding material. Rothwell (1971) reported an increase in erosion by a factor of 1.5 to 3 for a doubling in slope length. Choosing the correct slope shape is also important. Convex slopes are much more prone to erosion than rectilinear slopes or concavities (Haigh, 1979; Thornes, 1980), and convexities should be minimised during landform design.

On large sites, landform design should aim to manufacture several smaller catchment areas so that slope lengths are reduced. Surface water flow can be further arrested by the construction of 'contour berms', or bench terraces (Fournier, 1972) at regular intervals down the slope. In South Wales, berms are placed at 20 m vertical interval on restored opencast coal spoil, running at 2° to feed into the main, armoured drainage system (see Plate 16). Berms are akin to 'cross drains' in conventional forest drainage (Pyatt, 1990), but are easier to construct on sloping mineral spoil, and are less likely to erode. They should be of even gradient (<2°), the width of a bulldozer blade and slope slightly towards the hill. It is important that they are constructed as an integral part of overburden replacement so that they form part of the new landform, and are not imposed upon it. If constructed after landforming has taken place, cut and fill slopes should be no steeper than 27° so that they can be revegetated (see Chapter 6).

Slope aspect

The aspect of a slope can considerably affect its microclimate. Table 5.1, from Coppin and Richards (1990), summarises the main differences between southerly and northerly slopes. Differences are greater for slopes of steeper angles. Dark-coloured unvegetated spoils, for example colliery and opencast coal spoils, are particularly prone to heating on southerly slopes. Richardson (1958) reported temperatures at the soil surface of greater than 45°C for periods ranging between three and six hours on 16 successive days on a 30° south-facing slope in County Durham. Landform design should therefore aim to minimise areas of steep slopes with a southerly aspect. Where they exist, it may be necessary to plant drought-tolerant tree species.

Exposure

Landforms with large amplitudes are liable to suffer from exposure on their summits. Sympathetic landform design can reduce exposed areas, and also create more sheltered locations where tree species intolerant of exposure can be grown.

Landform and landscape

Mineral sites, even when restored, can look extremely artificial unless care is taken in

Table 5.1 Effects of aspect on microclimate (from Coppin and Richards, 1990)

Season	*Southerly aspects*	*Northerly aspects*
Winter	Wide range of diurnal temperatures with regular freeze–thaw cycles	Narrow range of diurnal temperatures, stays frozen/cold; snow cover protects vegetation from exposure
Spring	Rapid warming of soil, early start to growing season; early spells with soil moisture deficit	Delayed growing season, but very rare to experience soil moisture deficit
Summer	Extreme surface temperatures; very high soil moisture deficit for extended periods	Moderate surface temperatures; may avoid prolonged soil moisture deficits
Autumn	Growing season extends into cooler months; soil moisture deficit takes longer to be reduced by rainfall	Early end to growing season; early end to soil moisture deficit

Note: the effects of other aspects will be intermediate between north and south

matching the new landform with the surrounding landscape. For example, spoil tips can look very stark if regraded, with monotonous convexo-concave slopes. Usually it is not possible to rework much beyond the existing boundaries of the site, so that its form cannot be made to emulate the natural contours. More deliberate landform design is then important to make the regraded tips aesthetically acceptable – concavities and embayments, suitably emphasised at the planting stage, may help to produce a visually interesting landform. Angularities such as sharp edges, shoulders of corners and irregular lines produced during mineral extraction should also be removed during restoration to reduce the obtrusiveness of the site.

The ridge and furrow landform (p. 33) can appear very unnatural, especially in the early years when the tree crop has not completely covered the site. If the ridges are regimentally parallel to one another, the visual effect can be obtrusive. Lucas (1983) suggested that ridges could be laid out in curves, and length, width and spacing of ridges be varied to increase landscape diversity, and this has been achieved successfully in South Wales. In principle, there seems to be no good reason why the ridge and furrow system should not be modified to accommodate landscape interests, though silvicultural and engineering site requirements should not be unduly sacrificed.

Mineral sites such as limestone quarries can be incongruous in the landscape, but restoration can improve their appearance as well as create sites for tree planting. The shape of the quarry face should reflect the landform, and the scale should be in keeping with that of the surrounding countryside. Any undisturbed area above the working face should not be too thin or parallel to the skyline. Breaking the skyline should be avoided wherever possible. Shape should be asymmetrical (Forestry Commission, 1991b). It may be possible to adjust the shape of active quarries by extra excavation, and by reworking spoil tips within the quarry boundaries. 'Restoration blasting' has been used to construct varied shape sequences of rock screes, buttresses and headwalls which replicate natural dalesides well (Bailey and Gunn, 1991) (Chapter 9).

The principles behind the design of landform for landscape purposes are further discussed in the Forestry Commission's *Community woodland design guidelines* (Forestry Commission, 1991b), and by Lucas (1983).

Landform and wildlife habitats

Reclamation to forestry should also consider opportunities for creating wildlife habitats (Chapter 1). Restoration for wildlife should aim to maximise the diversity of landforms, water forms and vegetation within the physical limitations of the site (Green and Salter, 1987). Restoration will need to take account of habitats and wildlife populations, in the surrounding countryside and on the site, before mineral extraction – new landforms should be created with realistic objectives of attracting likely wildlife types. Once the wildlife species to be attracted have been identified, appropriate habitat types can be planned and included in the overall reclamation strategy. Landform plays a vital part in the success of a wildlife habitat, and the aims of a forestry scheme for wildlife should be determined well in advance of the restoration process. Wildlife habitats cannot be successfully imposed on a reclaimed site afterwards.

Landform features such as slope angle, orientation, shape and stability all affect the establishment of plants, which in turn affects habitat area, the amount of habitat edge and habitat diversity (Green and Salter, 1987). Landform design can also include special habitat features such as the retention of the highwall to create a cliff habitat for hole nesting bees, wasps and birds. Other features of quarries such as scree or talus slopes provide habitats for a number of small mammals and birds and are particularly valuable when provided in conjunction with highwall protection. Irregular topography – cliffs, rocks, gullies, steep slopes, depressions and small ponds – all benefit wildlife diversity (Steele and Grant, 1982). Diverse terrain provides protective cover from climatic extremes as well as from predators and human disturbance. This is of particular importance in the first years after reclamation when plant and tree cover is still immature.

Ponds, lakes, watercourses and wetlands are probably the most valuable introductions if the aims of reclamation include enhancement of wildlife. Water not only provides wildlife habitats itself, but also presents opportunities to create a variety of habitat edges associated with shorelines or stream banks. For example, willow shrublands thrive on saturated soils around water bodies, and provide forage for ungulates, cover for small mammals and birds and shade for fish (Green and Salter, 1987). Willows and other broadleaved species also support large numbers of insects, providing a valuable food source for foraging bats. The water's edge is particularly important for wildlife, and increasing its length by excavating bays of varying size and steepness will increase the quantity and variety of fauna and flora. Depth of water should also be varied, from between 15 cm and 2 m if dabbling ducks are to be encouraged, but between 60 cm and 2.5 m for diving ducks (Street, 1989). If fish are to be stocked, depths up to 3 m may be needed for some species such as trout. Shallow, sheltered inlets may be useful as spawning areas for amphibians.

Providing artificial nest and roost sites for waterfowl will help to protect birds from human interference. Long islands, with their long axes at 90° to the prevailing winds serve this purpose best. Islands can also be used to shelter some of the shallow water areas where ducks may be expected to feed (Street, 1983).

Development of water features can be combined with, and improve, water protection measures on a site: the features can act as siltation traps at times of high rainfall when soil erosion may occur, and as attenuation ponds during periods of flood flow (p. 32). Water bodies used during mining, such as silt lagoons, may, of course, be managed for wildlife after mineral extraction has ceased, rather than covered and soiled for conventional tree planting. Alternatively, lakes and ponds can be created deliberately to maximise the use of soil resources for areas where trees are to be planted. In addition, water bodies and water courses may be useful in fighting or preventing the spread of fires, once the tree crop has matured.

If open water bodies are to form part of a restored mineral site, then their desirability will be assessed in the normal legislative framework that controls the operation and reclamation of these sites, namely the Town and Country Planning Act (1990). The type of after-use will relate, in part, to the policies defined in the relevant county structure plan and local plans. Some types of water body also need permission and licensing from the local water authority or internal drainage board. If the pond or lake is constructed using a dam to impound the water, it may constitute a reservoir. Such a water body, if it has a volume greater than 25 000 cubic metres above the level of the surrounding ground, must have the dam designed by a specially qualified engineer and thereafter placed under the supervision of a qualified engineer as specified under the Reservoirs Act (1975).

Further guidance on the creation of wetland features is given by Street (1989), Andrews and Kinsman (1990) and Land Use Consultants (1992).

Landform and geological conservation

Mineral workings are often valuable for the geological exposures they present (Nature Conservancy Council, 1990). Restoration, especially that involving infilling with imported materials, tends to obscure or eliminate such features. Where exposures are considered worthy of preservation, it may be necessary to redesign the restored landform so that exposures are preserved, and made safe and accessible. Guidance on methods to preserve geological sections in mineral workings and landfill sites is given by the Nature Conservancy Council (1990) and Wilson and Thomas (1991). Advice on the identification of sites worthy of conservation can be obtained from English Nature, Scottish Natural Heritage and the Countryside Council for Wales (addresses in Appendix 6).

Roads

Roads are an often forgotten part of reclamation for forestry. Yet, as in conventional afforestation, they are essential for access to the plantation for planting, maintenance, fire fighting and harvesting; they may also be used by the public for recreational purposes, if access is permitted. Nevertheless, the construction of forest roads can represent a substantial cost in the restoration phase, and careful planning is required to determine a suitable density for present and future needs. Some forms of restoration, such as ridge and furrow (p. 33) may make cross-country travel difficult, and may warrant a greater density of roads than is usual in conventional forestry.

The planning of forest roads should take place well before mineral extraction begins, and their location should be decided in accordance with the plans for topography and drainage. Materials suitable for road construction may occur within the overburden; borehole and geophysical survey data can be used to identify them so that they can be retained for construction purposes later on.

Minimum standards for forest road construction are given in Table 5.2. Further information on road construction is given by Rowan (1976) and Hay (in production).

Table 5.2 Summary of forest road standards (from Hay, in production)

Feature	*Standard*	
Formation width	min. 4.7 m	
Camber	min. 75 mm	
Crossfall	min. 150 mm, but not exceeding 190 mm	
Gradient	min. 1%, max. 10%	
Road pavement width	min. 3.2 m	
Horizontal curves	radius (m)	road pavement width (m)
	60	3.8
	45	4.0
	30	4.4
	25	4.8
	20	5.4–5.5
	15	5.9–6.4
Pavement thickness	150 – 450 mm	
Turning places	4 m width; 21 m length	
Passing places	4 m width; 33 m length	

Soil replacement

After a site has been landformed, usually using overburden materials, soils must be replaced. These may include soil-forming materials, or materials brought onto the site from elsewhere to supplement or replace those lost. On sites worked progressively, soil which has been stripped prior to mineral working may be moved directly to a newly restored phase – the soil undergoes no storage on site. On most sites, however, some or most soil materials are put into storage until landforming has been completed.

Soil replacement is one of the most important operations in reclamation (Ramsay, 1986). If performed injudiciously, for example in poor weather conditions, considerable damage can occur, and may be impossible to rectify. In particular, soils may suffer compaction, with consequent effects on available water capacity, aeration status and root penetration (Chapter 2).

Various methods of replacing soils on overburden exist. Traditionally, earthscrapers have been used as the primary means of both stripping and replacing soil materials. They probably offer the simplest and most economical method of bulk soil movement. However, operator control over earthmoving contractors has often been poor (Ramsay, 1986). A major problem has been the running of scrapers over soil previously laid down, causing serious compaction. If scrapers have to be employed, placement of soil should start at the furthest point from soil stores so that the scraper hauls over the surface of the overburden rather than the soil materials already spread. Reinstatement should take place in strips, using carefully planned haul routes, and random passes outlawed by effective site supervision.

Even if carefully planned and executed, soil replacement by earthscrapers will inevitably cause soil compaction (Ramsay, 1986), and will require relieving by cultivation operations (see Chapter 6). An alternative system which has been developed for agricultural restoration over the last 15 to 20 years is the dumptruck and excavator method (Bransden, 1991).

Excavators (backactors) are used for both soil lifting and placement, and dumptrucks for transport. Dumptrucks move soil from store or from the new phase being stripped to the strip being restored, and tip it in heaps on the surface of the overburden. From a position on the surface of the fill, the soil is then spread and levelled using a tracked hydraulic excavator with a wide bucket (see Plates 17–19). If topsoil is to be replaced, this is then brought in and placed in heaps on the fill adjacent to the levelled subsoil. From here, it can be lifted by the excavator and spread over the subsoil (see Figure 5.2). When the topsoil has been laid over the first strip, the next strip is started using the same cycle of operations. At no stage is any soil trafficked by earthmoving machinery, and compaction can be almost entirely avoided (Department of the Environment, 1986). Work can continue at higher moisture contents than with other systems because soils are never subjected to compressive forces (Ramsay, 1986).

1. Soil materials brought in by dump truck running on overburden.

2. Soil materials tipped in heaps onto overburden.

3. Soil materials spread and levelled by hydraulic excavator from overburden surface.

Figure 5.2 Schematic diagram illustrating loose tipping (from Dobson and Moffat, 1993).

Depending on the thickness of soil layers to be replaced, it may be necessary to rip (see Chapter 6) the surface of the overburden prior to soil placement, to allow roots to ramify into the overburden once they have extended through the soil above. However, if the 'loose tipping' method of soil replacement is performed properly, it should not be necessary to rip or cultivate the soil materials.

The two main methods of soil placement have been the subject of forestry research, in the restoration of opencast coal sites, sand and gravel workings and landfill.

Opencast coal spoil

Rip plough cultivation has been employed since the early 1970s in an attempt to relieve compaction in spoil materials on restored opencast coal spoil. Loose tipping methods have recently been tested at the Maesgwyn site in Mid Glamorgan. Figure 5.3 shows the comparative effectiveness of two methods using penetration resistance as a measure of compaction. Cultivation relieves compaction, but the main effect is restricted to the upper 20 cm, and the effect is shortlived: substantial recompaction takes place within six months of cultivation. The loose tipped material is, in contrast, much less compact to a considerably greater depth, and recompaction takes place to a much smaller extent. Current research is evaluating the effect of loose tipping on root extension and tree growth.

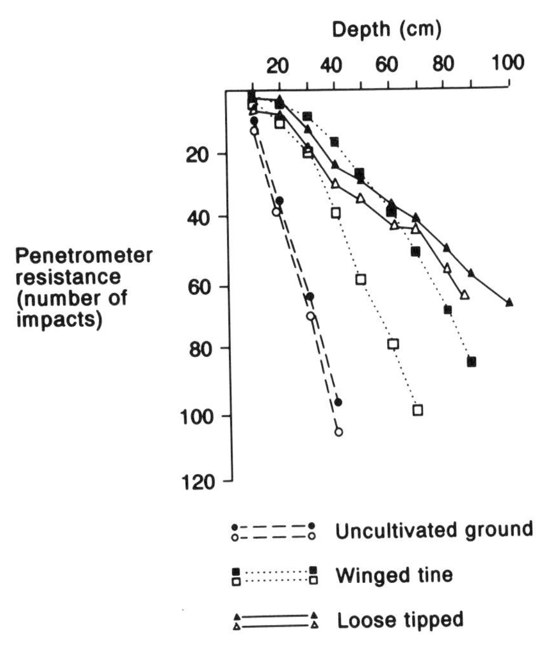

Closed symbols represent June 1990 assessments
Open symbols represent February 1991 assessments.

Figure 5.3 Comparison of spoil penetration resistance following cultivation and loose tipping on opencast coal spoils in South Wales.

Sand and gravel

The efficacy of ripping soils on restored sand and gravel workings has recently been questioned by Moffat and Roberts (1989c). They found that six years after ripping, soil bulk densities were generally high, demonstrating that recompaction had taken place. As a consequence, tree root depth was inhibited, and growth restricted by drought. Figure 5.4 shows the average penetration resistance for 30 m ridges restored in two ways: a. constructed conventionally, then ripped to relieve compaction, and b. by loose tipping. The results demonstrate that loose tipping produces a less compact substrate, whereas on the conventional ripped ridge, compaction is significantly greater, especially below 30 cm.

Landfill

Comparison of survival, after five years, of trees planted on conventionally ripped, ripped and disced, and loose tipped clayey spoil material at a landfill site in Bedfordshire is shown in Figure 5.5. Survival is markedly improved in the loose tipped material for all species tested.

Loose tipping is practised in other countries, especially in the placement of overburden or soil-forming materials (Geyer and Rogers, 1972; Daniels and Amos, 1984). As the inadequacy of cultivation fully to relieve soil compaction becomes better known, there is likely to be a greater impetus to advocate loose tipping as a soil placement method for forestry schemes. An additional argument is

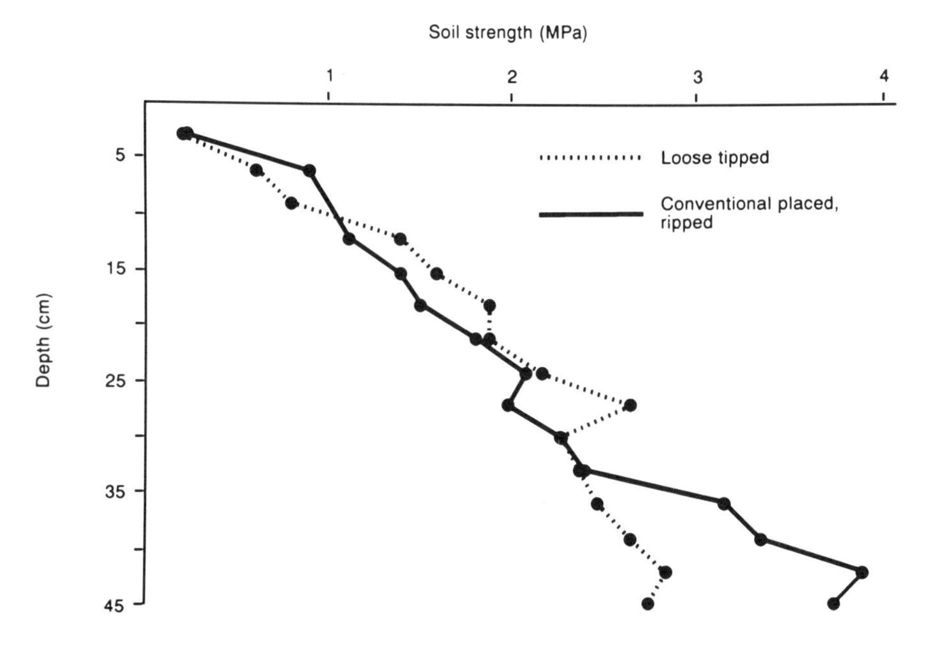

Figure 5.4 Comparison of soil penetration resistance following cultivation and loose tipping on restored sand and gravel workings in Hampshire.

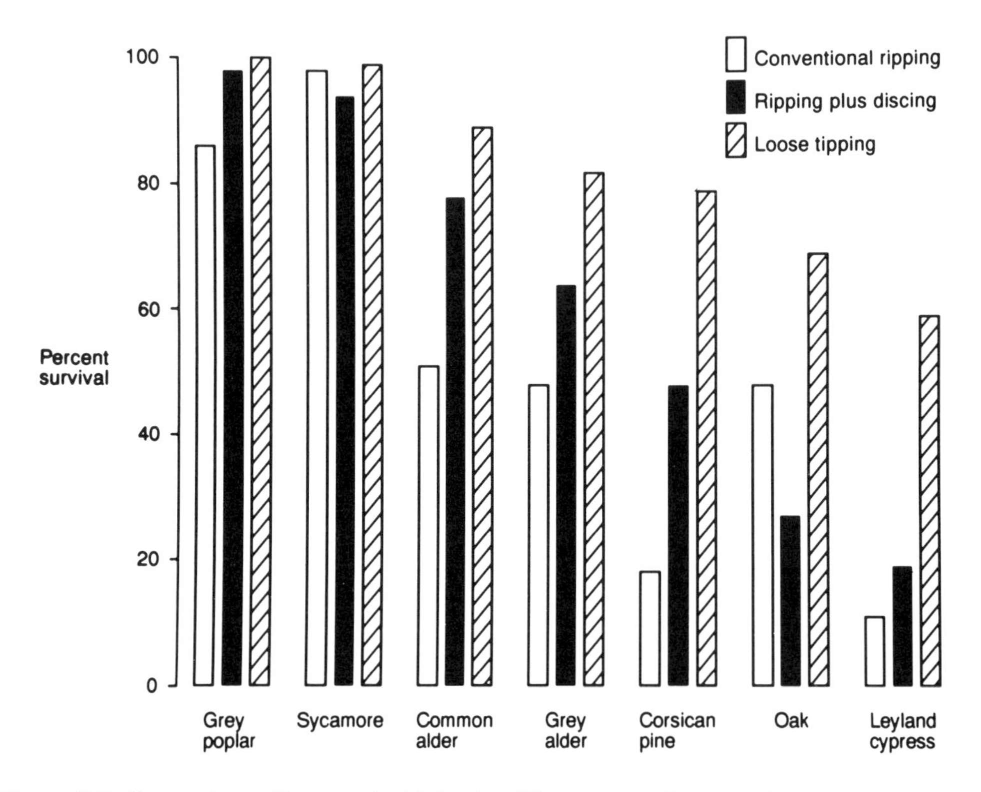

Figure 5.5 Comparison of tree survival following different ground preparation operations on a landfill site in Bedfordshire.

that, unlike in agricultural after-uses, there is only one opportunity to relieve compaction – in the season before tree planting takes place. If recompaction occurs, it cannot be relieved after the trees are planted. It is imperative therefore that, as far as possible, compaction is **prevented** in the first place, rather than attempts made to **cure** it.

Soil replacement using materials held in storage mounds requires especial care because these materials will, inevitably, have suffered compaction (p. 29). The excavator should use long shallow strokes of the bucket when loading soil into the dump truck as this helps to break up the compacted material (Bransden, 1991).

Topsoil mounds may also warrant a sequential approach to their stripping, because their upper surface layer can provide valuable populations of earthworms that are absent from deeper layers. This material can then be used in patches across the restored site to provide sources for its colonisation by earthworms, to the benefit of soil structure (Scullion, 1991).

Soil thickness

An important consideration, for the restoration of both mineral workings and derelict land, is the thickness of soil, or soil-forming materials, necessary for placement as final cover in which trees will be planted. On modern mineral sites, soil materials are likely to be saved and replaced. However, if forestry is the planned after-use following mineral extraction, it is important to examine whether existing soil resources will sustain a tree crop over its life. If there is an expected shortage in the soil needed to make up a minimum thickness, soil-forming materials from the overburden should be identified and saved; on derelict sites, it will be important to assess how much soil, or soil substitute, must be imported.

Figures 5.6 to 5.9 (located with Plates 15 and 16) give guidance on the minimum soil thickness needed for a **mature** stand of trees to extract moisture from the soil and transpire it at optimal rates during summer months. The figures show that there are wide differences in minimum soil thickness required to support mature tree crops in different parts of England and Wales. Loamy soils, with relatively high available water capacities (p. 12), provide the most plant available water per unit depth, and hence the required soil thicknesses are relatively small. Stony, sandy soils contain little plant available water, and large thicknesses are required in the drier parts of eastern England.

Appendix 7 gives more detail about the calulation of soil thickness. Despite the assumptions made, the model demonstrates the need to appreciate moisture supply to a maturing crop when planning the size of soil thickness at restoration.

Chapter 6
Aftercare

Introduction

In mineral reclamation, aftercare includes all operations necessary to establish and maintain the after-use of a restored site. For forestry, this can include cultivation, ground vegetation establishment, tree planting, weed control, protection from animals, fertilizing and tending, depending upon the particular requirements of the crop. This Chapter describes these operations in some detail; its contents apply equally to derelict land and landfill reclamation.

The aftercare period

Planning permission for mineral working will normally be subject to aftercare conditions, as laid down in the Town and Country Planning Act (1990). These can be imposed in one of two forms:

1 an aftercare condition imposed at the time of granting permission, specifying the steps to be taken; or

2 a condition which allows an aftercare scheme to be submitted by the mineral operator or other appropriate person for approval by the mineral planning authority.

The Department of the Environment Minerals Planning Guidance Note 7 (1989) suggests that the second method will usually be more appropriate where restoration and aftercare may not start for a number of years.

The Town and Country Planning Act (1990) stipulates that the aftercare period should be up to a maximum of five years. However, five years is barely long enough for forest establishment to be assured (Teasdale, 1983). In the context of restored mineral workings, the first growing season for the planted trees cannot occur before the second of the five years. This leaves only a short time for the trees to become sufficiently established for fertiliser needs to be determined. It is important, therefore, for aftercare operations to start as soon as the aftercare period begins; if restoration activities can be completed in late winter or early spring, the first aftercare operations, especially cultivation, can begin without a break. This will allow planting the following winter. This ideal transition from restoration to aftercare will depend on suitable weather and ground conditions, but it should be attempted if at all possible.

The length of the aftercare period can be varied by the Secretary of State by regulation, though this power is rarely used. However, if both operator and mineral planning authority agree to a longer period, this can be provided for through an agreement under Section 106 of the 1990 Planning Act. Uptake of an establishment grant under the Woodland Grant Scheme (Appendix 1) also ensures that the new plantation is scrutinised for a period of ten years by the Forestry Authority.

Cultivation

Compaction is the invariable accompaniment of soil movement. And unless soils are replaced by loose tipping (see Chapter 5), cultivation will normally be required to bring the soil into a state for planting and root growth. Choice of cultivation will depend on site characteristics such as ground formation, presence of large boulders or buried debris, slope, soil texture and soil depth.

The most common form of cultivation in forest reclamation involves the use of deep tines, usually to a depth of 0.5 m (clay sites) or 0.7 m (sandy sites). A set of three to five tines is carried on a parallelogram mounting behind a powerful tractor unit, preferably tracked. Straight shank tines (unwinged) can be used but were originally developed for quarry ripping and the amount of ground disturbance is limited. Nevertheless, increase in tree growth following ripping in this way can be marked (Jobling and Carnell, 1985) (see Figure 6.1).

The winged tine (Fourt, 1978, 1979, 1980b) (see Figure 6.2 and Plate 20) is capable of considerably more ground disturbance, and is generally recommended for cultivation to alleviate soil compaction. However, it can be vulnerable to buried rocks and other large debris, and may be unsuitable for some types of overburden unless stone picking operations precede cultivation. Tines should preferably be spaced no more than 1.2 m apart, with the outer ones positioned in line with the tractor tracks. Ripping is generally carried out in a downhill direction, unless slope makes this unsafe. On the ridge and furrow landform (see

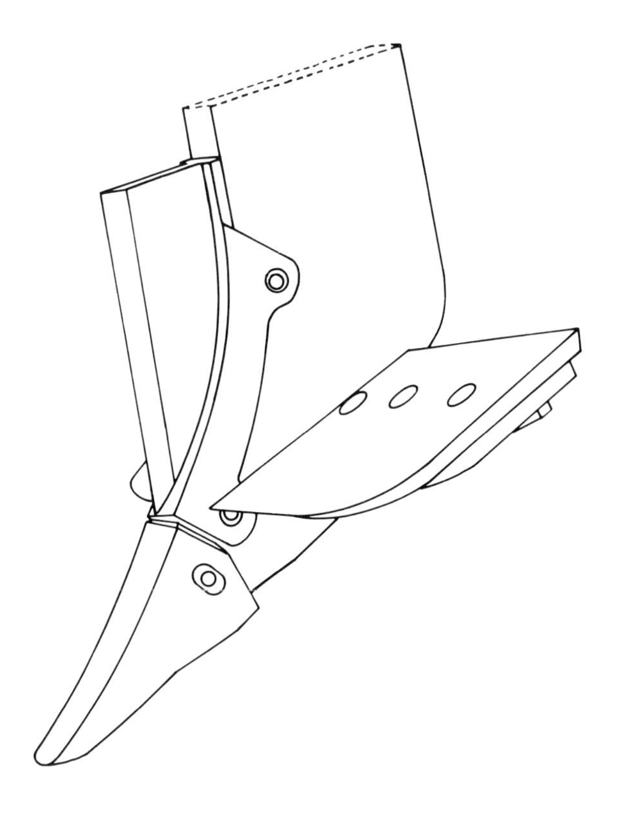

Figure 6.2 Diagram showing the design of the winged tine.

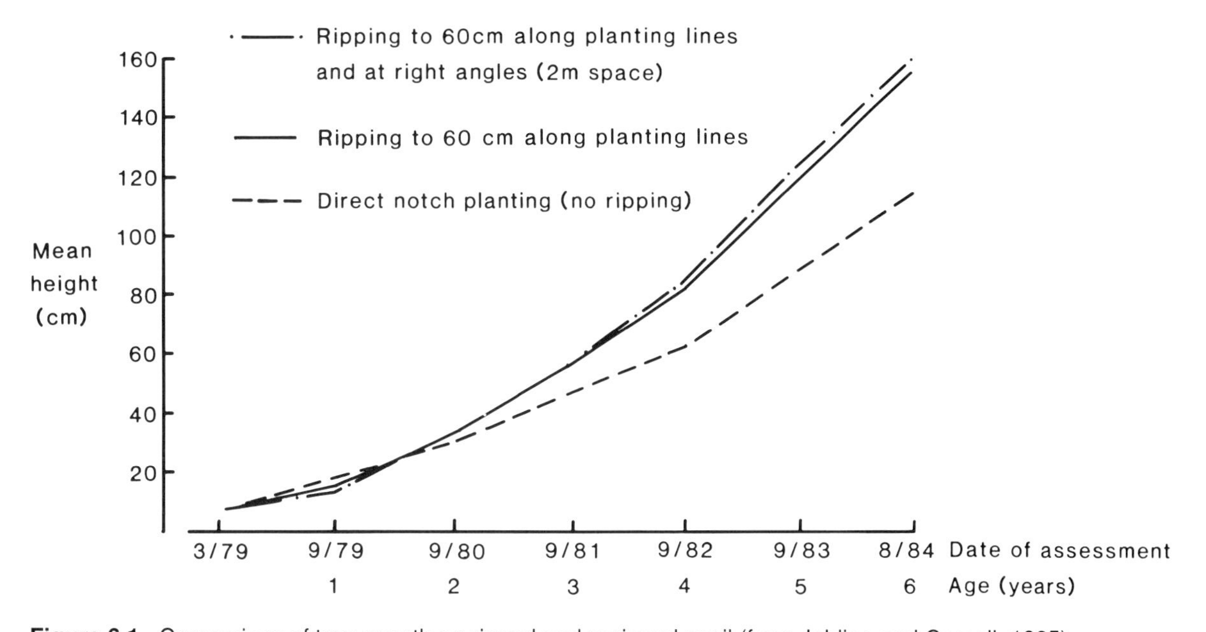

Figure 6.1 Comparison of tree growth on ripped and unripped spoil (from Jobling and Carnell, 1985).

Chapter 5), ripping should take place across the ridges to facilitate drainage into the furrows. On porous materials, a final pass with the ripper can be made along the furrow bottom to encourage downward drainage.

In some regions, heavy discs are often used as a final treatment to break up stony material that may have been brought to the surface during ripping, or to incorporate materials such as cake sewage sludge into the soil. Discs can also form a small planting ridge if they are set towards each other on the tool bar. However, it is not recommended that discs alone are used as a form of cultivation because the depth of penetration is rarely enough to relieve compaction properly.

In small areas, and on steep embankments, complete ground cultivation may be severely restricted or even impossible. On these sites, a 360° excavator can sometimes be used to loosen soils or spoils. As a last resort, an excavator or mechanical auger should be used to prepare pits of loosened material at each planting position. However, it is important that the trees can exploit sufficient soil volume as they mature, and this is often underestimated when planning the size of the pit.

Cultivation operations such as ripping and discing should always take place in the summer months when the soil is driest. If the soil is at all wet, deep ripping may fail to relieve compaction; the tine simply forms a subsurface channel, and little or no heaving and shattering takes place. In a very wet year, cultivation may have to be postponed until the next dry summer.

Ground cover

The need to establish a herbaceous ground cover will depend on a number of factors including the need for erosion control, encouragement of soil formation, improvement of soil nutrient capital, nature conservation (e.g. a desire to establish native herbs and shrubs) or aesthetic requirements, such as a need for general 'greening' of a site. Where trees are planted into a vegetation cover, whether artificially sown or arising from natural invasion, there will be severe competition for moisture, light, space and nutrients. Localised vegetation control around each tree will usually be necessary (p. 50).

An option sometimes put forward is to plant trees on a site deliberately kept totally free of ground vegetation cover (the 'scorched earth' policy). This is unacceptable on those reclaimed sites where there is a high risk of erosion, or where ground vegetation is necessary to initiate soil formation. In addition, constant application of some herbicides can induce chemical build-up in the soil, which in turn leads to deleterious effects on the trees.

Ground vegetation cover can consist of two main types: grass dominated, and legume dominated.

- Grasses – grass swards are easy to establish, and there are many mixtures suitable for reclamation sites available on the market. However, some species can compete strongly with trees for moisture and nutrients, e.g. rye grass (*Lolium perenne*) and red fescue (*Festuca rubra*) (Insley and Buckley, 1980). Competition can be reduced by using lower than recommended sowing rates, or incorporating undemanding or less vigorous species. A low-competitive-species mixture suitable for sowing amongst trees on most reclamation substrates is:

Agrostis capillaris	10%
Festuca rubra var. *commutata*	20%
Festuca ovina / *F. tenuifolia*	40%
Trifolium repens	20%
Lotus corniculatus	10%

(Coppin and Bradshaw, 1982)

For opencast coal spoils in South Wales, a mixture containing *Festuca rubra* var. *rubra*, *Poa pratensis*, *Poa compressa*, *Agrostis tenuis*, *Festuca longifolia* and *Onobrychis viciifolia* was recommended by Moffat and Roberts (1990).

In general, fertiliser applications to promote grass growth are not considered necessary or desirable. A better, and more self-sustaining, approach is to use grass mixtures which contain a proportion of legume species.

Plate 15 Erosion on unvegetated coal spoil.

Plate 16 Contour berm on restored opencast coal site, South Wales.

5.6 Stoneless loamy soil.

5.7 Stoneless sandy soil.

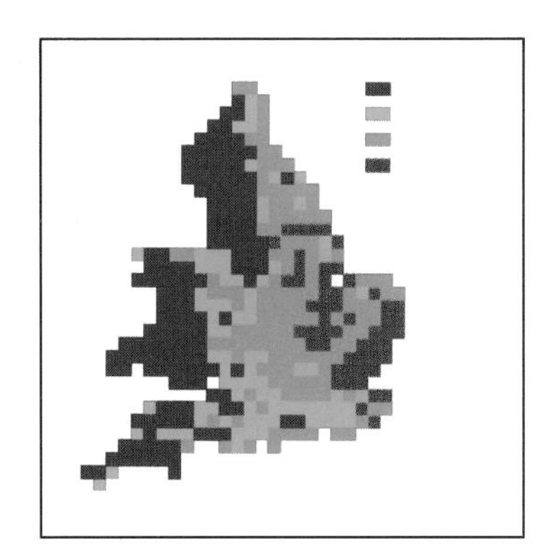

5.8 Stony (30% by volume) loamy soil.

5.9 Stony (30% by volume) sandy soil.

Figures 5.6–5.9 Soil depth needed to satisfy the water requirements of a mature tree crop on various soils, in cm.

Plates 17–19
Loose tipping of peat:
17. Material brought to final site by dumptruck;
18. Grading of peat using 360° excavator;
19. Restored peat surface, Ayrshire.

Plate 20 Tine assembly on a Caterpillar D8 (300hp); the two outer tines are winged; depth of working 750 mm.

- Legumes – leguminous plant species have a symbiotic relationship with the bacteria *Rhizobium* spp. which forms nodules on the roots. This process allows plants to 'fix' and store atmospheric nitrogen which may subsequently be of benefit to trees interplanted with them. A number of species have been used successfully on a range of restored sites (Moffat *et al.*, 1989): they can be sown either as a pure legume cover (see Plates 21 and 22) or in mixtures with grasses. Site characteristics will affect choice of species, and Table 6.1 provides useful information on selection. It is usually desirable to sow a mixture of legumes, to increase the chance that ground cover will be achieved.

Most leguminous herbs and shrubs can be established from seed sowing, but sometimes it is preferable to plant the larger growing shrubs as individual plants to reduce site dominance and achieve more accurate spacing. Seed sowing is more effective on friable materials, free from compaction and large amounts of stone or rock.

Seed of some species of legume require mechanical scarification to break dormancy, notably lupin and pea species (Best, 1983). All legume seed should be inoculated with the appropriate strain of *Rhizobia* before sowing. Inoculants are available commercially for most leguminous species from the Agricultural Genetics Company Ltd (address in Appendix 6).

Tree planting

This section discusses the principles behind tree establishment on disturbed land, and gives guidance on species choice and appropriate techniques for planting and tending.

Table 6.1 Legumes suitable for sowing as a ground vegetation cover (derived from Jefferies, 1981; Vogel, 1987)

Species	*Lifespan*	*Soil pH range*	*Nutrient demand*	*Tolerance of*	
				drought	*waterlogging*
Tree lupin (*Lupinus arboreus*)	short-lived	4.5–7.0	L	T	MT
Everlasting pea (*Lathyrus sylvestris, L. latifolius*)	perennial	4.0–7.5	L	T	MT
White clover (*Trifolium repens*)	perennial	5.5–7.0	VH	S	MT
Red clover (*Trifolium pratense*)	biennial	5.0–7.5	VH	MT	S
Birdsfoot trefoil (*Lotus corniculatus*)	perennial	4.5–8.0	M	T	MT
Sainfoin (*Onobrychis viciifolia*)	short-lived	6.5–8.0	M	T	T
Lotus 'maku' (*Lotus uliginosus*)	perennial	4.0–7.0	M	MT	T
Lucerne (*Medicago sativa*)	perennial	5.5–8.0	VH	T	S

L: low; M: moderate; VH: very high; S: sensitive; MT: moderately tolerant; T: tolerant

Species

The choice of tree species is a very important element in the reclamation of man-made sites to a woodland cover. Choice will be determined by the objectives of tree establishment and by site conditions; the latter should take precedence over the former. In other words, it is important that trees are planted that will actually *grow* on the site in question. A general policy on man-made sites is to select comparatively undemanding, or 'pioneer', species.

Site conditions which should influence species choice include availability of topsoil, soil wetness status, soil chemical reaction (pH), pollution level, local climate and exposure. In addition, planning requirements (e.g. a preference for native woodland species), wildlife, amenity and recreational needs, and timber production requirements will affect choice of species. Table 6.2 identifies species most likely to be suited to planting conditions on reclaimed sites. The list is deliberately conservative and assumes that sites are impaired nutritionally compared with undisturbed substrates. However, if restoration involves the use of topsoil, more demanding species such as ash can be considered. Spruce should only be used in high rainfall areas, while Douglas fir and beech are too site-demanding for normal consideration. Species indicative of ancient woodland, such as wild service tree and spindle, have no place in tree planting schemes on disturbed soils or spoils.

Mixtures

There is a desire on many reclaimed sites for tree planting to be in groups or intimate mixtures of different species, as this is perceived as visually more attractive and ecologically more diverse than monocultures or simple row mixtures. Some tree species can also provide a benefit to others in terms of shelter and nutrition. Alders are especially suitable for this purpose being able to establish quickly on a range of infertile sites (Moffat *et al.*, 1989). Alders are an **actinorhizal** group of trees – they fix nitrogen through their symbiotic relationship with the micro-organism *Frankia* spp. which forms nodules on the roots. There is good evidence that on infertile sites, nitrogen demanding species can gain nutritionally by being planted in a mixture with alder. It is essential that alder stock is well nodulated at the time of planting; unnodulated stock should be rejected as unsuitable because it grows poorly in comparison (see Plate 23).

Although often found close to water, alders grow better in soils that are not permanently waterlogged. Of six species that have been tested for use on reclamation sites, two – Sitka alder (*Alnus sinuata*) and green alder (*A. viridis*) – have shrubby habits. Green alder can produce a considerable amount of biomass, without competing with other components of the mixture (Vann *et al.*, 1988) . The other four species (common alder, grey alder, red alder, Italian alder) are faster growing and on very poor sites can shade, abrade and suppress other trees in the mixture, particularly at close spacing or in an intimate alternate single plant mixture. In these circumstances it may be necessary to cut back or coppice the alder component, though careful spacing or choice of mixture pattern can help to minimise the effects.

Other mixtures which have shown promise include Sitka spruce in mixture with Japanese larch on opencast coal spoils in Scotland, and Corsican pine with green alder on china clay spoils in Cornwall (Chapter 9).

Stock type and size

It is normal practice to plant restored sites with trees which have been raised in the protected environment of a nursery. Plant types range from small seedlings to large standards. However, past experience has shown that larger plants are generally more difficult to establish, particularly where topsoil is not available or where the site is prone to vandalism. In contrast, very small plants are susceptible to frost lift and weed competition. Transplants, undercuts and containerised plants are the most suitable stock type for almost all man-made sites.

- Transplants are small trees – less than 1.2 m tall and up to three or four years old.

Table 6.2 Suitable tree species for reclaimed man-made sites

Species are classified as tolerant (••), moderately tolerant (•), or intolerant (X) to heavy soils (likely to be seasonally waterlogged), calcareous soils, acidic soils, exposure and air pollution

Species	*Heavy soils*	*Calcareous soils*	*Acidic soils*	*Exposure*	*Air pollution*	*Comments*
Broadleaves						
Ash	X	••	X	X	X	Fertile sites only
Common alder	••	•	•	•	••	Nitrogen-fixing
Crack willow	••	••	X	X	•	
Downy birch	•	X	•	••	••	
English oak	•	•	•	•	•	Fertile sites only
False acacia	•	•	••	X	••	Nitrogen-fixing
Field maple	•	••	•	•	•	
Goat willow	•	•	•	X	••	
Grey alder	••	•	•	•	•	Nitrogen-fixing
Grey poplar	••	••	•	••	••	
Hawthorn	•	•		••	••	
Italian alder	•	••	X	X	••	Nitrogen-fixing
Norway maple	•	••	X	••	•	
Red alder	••	X	•	••	•	Nitrogen-fixing
Red oak	•	•	••	•	•	
Rowan	•	•	•	••	•	
Silver birch	X	X	••	••	••	
Swedish whitebeam	••	•	•	•	•	
Sycamore	•	••	•	••	••	
Whitebeam	••	••	••	•	•	
White poplar	••	X	•	••	••	
Wild cherry	X	•	X	X	•	Fertile sites only
Conifers						
Corsican pine	•	••	••	••	••	Below 250 m OD
European larch	•	X	•	•	X	
Japanese larch	•	X	•	•	•	
Lodgepole pine	••	X	••	•	X	North only
Scots pine	X	X	••	••	X	
Sitka spruce	•	•	•	••	X	Fertile sites only

They are raised as seedlings for up to two years then transplanted for a further year to improve growth and root development. Transplants are identified in categories depending upon the number of years at each stage, eg 1+1, 1½+1½, 2+1.

- Undercuts are the same size as transplants but are precision sown, grown as normal seedlings for the first season or part season, and then undercut in the bed where they are growing to sever side and downward-growing roots. This treatment improves plant root mass and controls tree height and growth. Undercut planting stock is identified in a similar way to transplants, e.g. ½*u*½, 1*u*1,1*u*1*u*1.
- Container grown plants are available in a variety of sizes, ages and types. However, for planting large areas, small, young plants are generally most suitable. Containers may be particularly good for improving the establishment of sensitive species such as Corsican pine (Coppock, 1986), but there may also be a general benefit to many other species due to the minimal root disturbance at planting. There can be a temptation to neglect containerised plants, by leaving them in their containers too long or planting at an inappropriate time. However, survival is likely to be reduced because of the imbalance in the shoot to root. Container grown plants are usually more expensive than transplants of a similar size.

The size of planting stock can considerably affect survival and, for reclamation sites, it is desirable to choose sturdy plants with a good stem diameter to height ratio. Jobling and Stevens (1980) give specifications for minimum diameter for four height classes of common tree species (see Table 6.3). These specifications are somewhat more exacting than BS3936, Part 4 (British Standards Institution, 1984), but probably have general applicability for a range of man-made sites. Minimum and maximum specifications for stem height at planting are difficult to give because of the large number of factors to be taken into account, but there is some agreement that broadleaved stock of between 300 and 600 mm is desirable. A height range of 100 to 200 mm is acceptable for conifers. Larger than normal trees tend to 'socket', and can be abraded against the sides of the planting hole as they are buffeted by the wind.

Table 6.3 Minimum diameter specifications for trees planted on coal spoils (from Jobling and Stevens, 1980)

	Minimum stem diameter at root collar (mm)			
	Height classes (mm)			
Species	*200*	*300*	*450*	*600*
Alders			10.5	14.0
Ash			9.0	11.0
Birches			7.0	9.0
Blackthorn			8.0	11.0
Common oak		6.5	8.5	
Common thorn			6.5	9.0
False acacia			7.0	10.0
Larches		5.0	7.0	
Maples			9.0	12.0
Pines	5.0	7.0		
Red oak		6.5	8.5	
Swedish whitebeam			9.5	13.0
White poplar			9.0	12.0
White willow			7.0	11.0

Handling

The length of time that plants spend out of the soil, between lifting in the nursery and planting on the site, must be as short as possible if losses are to be avoided. This is particularly important when difficult or harsh site conditions are likely to be encountered.

Bare root planting stock is lifted and size graded when dormant (late autumn onwards), and then fully enclosed and secured in co-extruded polythene bags for either cold storage or transportation to planting sites. Bagged plants can be stored for a short period of time away from sunlight and where there is a low ambient temperature, e.g. in a cool shed or under a dense tree canopy.

At the planting site, bagged plants can be left in the open in cool shade but only for a few days. When plants are removed from the polythene bags for planting, they must be put immediately in planting bags carried by the planting staff. This will ensure that plant roots remain covered for protection against desiccation. To minimise damage during transit, tree bags should never be handled roughly, dropped on the ground or packed tightly together.

Containerised plants can arrive at the planting site still in the original production containers, though some nurseries prefer to remove the containers prior to dispatch, and transport the stock in bags or boxes. In that case, the plants should be handled with the same care as bare-root stock.

Planting method

The choice of planting method will depend on the size and type of plant stock used, and on the form of site cultivation. If transplants, undercuts and smaller types of container stock are used, notch planting is generally the most suitable method. This involves cutting a notch in the soil with a spade, and keeping the notch open while the tree roots are carefully inserted and spread downwards. The notch must be carefully firmed, using toe pressure, whilst pulling the tree slightly upwards to ensure that the original root collar is aligned with the ground surface (see Figure 6.3).

Notch planting is unsuitable for planting trees in clayey soils, or for larger planting stock and containerised plants. Pit planting should be used in these circumstances. This

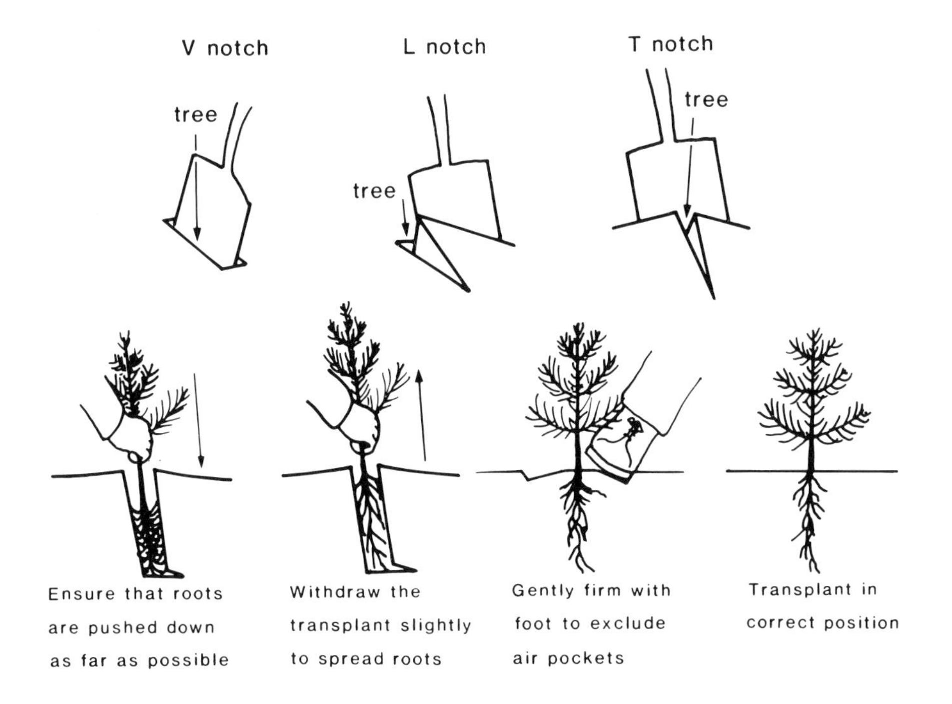

Figure 6.3 Diagram to illustrate notch planting of trees (from Dobson and Moffat, 1993).

involves digging a pit to accommodate the complete root ball, without bending any of the roots. The soil should be carefully replaced and firmed around the plant, as in notch planting, with the root collar in line with the ground level. Container stock should always be removed from the container before planting; even biodegradable containers can inhibit root growth if left attached. In forestry planting, the use of soil ameliorants, such as peat or peat-substitutes, in the pit back fill is not considered necessary or desirable (Potter, 1989).

On substrates that have been cultivated, it is important to choose the planting position carefully in relation to the micro-topography left by the cultivation tool. Trees planted in the bottom of a ripper, disc or plough channel tend to develop roots preferentially along the channel, and are therefore potentially liable to become unstable (Edwards *et al.*, 1963). Plants in this position can also suffer from waterlogging, possibly resulting in root death. Planting on the raised rip, disc or plough ridge is generally preferred, but depends on the size, shape and height of the ridge. On some sites, perching plants on a high ridge may place them in a vulnerable, exposed or droughty position. A sensible compromise is to plant them on the sides of the ridges.

Time of planting

Trees should be planted when they are dormant, usually in the period from late autumn to early spring; dates will vary throughout the country according to site location and climate. In northern Britain, it is usually impossible to plant in midwinter due to snow and frozen ground. The spring planting period can be extended, using plants which have been kept in dormancy by cold storage, but planting should always be accomplished by the end of March, irrespective of plant storage.

Spacing

A number of factors, including site characteristics and choice of tree species, influence tree spacing, but a distance of 2 m is normal in

British forestry. This gives a stocking density of 2500 plants per hectare. On infertile reclaimed sites, where tree growth may be expected to be slow, a closer spacing may be advisable to hasten the closure of the canopy. Plants should be spaced regularly in rows where possible, and this is often dictated by the ridges formed during ploughing or ripping operations. Regular spacing facilitates the management of subsequent tending operations such as beating up, weeding and fertilising.

Direct tree seeding

The idea that woodland can be established by direct seed sowing, in place of planting nursery tree stock, became popular for the reclamation of man-made sites in the 1980s (e.g. Luke and Macpherson, 1983; La Dell, 1983). Direct tree seeding was considered to have a number of advantages, including its perceived low cost and its ability to establish a range of diverse plant communities (Luke and Macpherson, 1983). The costs of seed and sowing were viewed as considerably smaller than the costs of tree stock and planting. In addition, cost savings were thought possible in the aftercare because a seeded area was expected to be self thinning (La Dell, 1983).

Direct seeding also has some disadvantages, principally the unpredictability of success and irregular stocking (Stevens *et al.*, 1990). The difficulties of preparing an adequate seedbed (Buckley, 1984), and weed competition and predation (Stevens *et al.*, 1990) are the main reasons for poor stocking. Buckley (1984) has suggested that germination and early survival may be as low as 5% of the viable seed sown.

There have been few rigorous studies to compare direct seeding with conventional tree planting. Luke *et al.* (1987) studied, in an unreplicated trial, the seeding of oak, rowan, Scots pine, birch and four shrub species on a sand quarry face in Bedfordshire. They found that two of the species (rowan and birch) showed no signs of germination after five months, and that the shrubs (especially lupins) were considerably more successful than the trees which germinated (oak and pine). In contrast, survival of planted trees ranged from 50% to 98% with pine and oak consistently successful across planted plots.

Putwain *et al.* (1988) studied the establishment of amenity woodland on roadsides by direct seeding. They found that of 13 tree and shrub species, only one species – broom – emerged in significant numbers in the first growing season, and the majority did not germinate until between 18 and 22 months after sowing. The emergence of four species was very poor, and the health of those that did germinate declined dramatically over the next few years.

Despite enthusiasm in the 1980s, it would appear that direct tree seeding can not yet be recommended as a reliable method for establishing woodland on reclaimed mineral workings and derelict land. This is especially so where a site is subject to a five year aftercare period. In such a short period of time, it is important that a plantation of acceptable species composition and stocking density is achieved, and conventional planting methods are the only ones that can achieve these aims.

Weed control

Where weed or sown vegetation is present, weeding will normally be needed around each tree position to remove the threat of physical suppression or competition for water and nutrients (Davies, 1987a). Research has shown that tree survival and growth are very significantly reduced by the presence of weeds. Weed control is best achieved by using approved chemical herbicides suitable for forestry use. Several herbicides are available, some acting systemically through the leaves, others being applied to the soil and taking effect through the roots. The range of suitable herbicides, and guidelines on their use, are contained in Forestry Commission Field Book 8 (Williamson and Lane, 1989).

Where weed or vegetation control is required, a weed free area of one metre in diameter around each tree position has been shown to provide effective relief from competition. Herbicide control will normally be needed during the first three growing seasons, but depends on how soon the trees become fully established. For maximum survival rate and growth, newly planted trees should be free from weed competition from the start of the first growing season. Restored sites can vary enormously in their weed populations, and the need for herbicide applications should be assessed periodically throughout the growing season.

Mulch mats made of black polythene are also useful in weed control. They act by smothering or preventing the establishment of weeds, and can be effective for two to three years (Potter, 1989). Mulch mats may be a better method in situations where herbicide weed control cannot be guaranteed.

On some sites, where a grass ground cover is established under the young trees to improve the visual appearance, there is sometimes a temptation to mow the grass, especially in areas frequented by the public. However, mowing invigorates the sward, and leads to increased moisture deficits and deleterious effects on the trees (Davies, 1987a). Mechanical weeding and strimming can also damage trees when cutting close to the stem. These practices should be avoided.

Tree protection

A number of small and large mammals – including voles, rabbits, hares, squirrels, deer and farm livestock – can cause damage to trees by bark stripping, browsing or burrowing. Trees can be damaged seriously or killed if they are not protected from these animals, and they may equally need protecting from humans in their early years.

Fencing

The most common protection for woodland areas greater than two hectares is fencing (Pepper, 1992). The type and specification should be stipulated in a planning condition, taking full account of the need to exclude likely animal predators, as well as to erect fencing for public safety under the Mines and Quarries Act (1954). On areas smaller than two hectares, other forms of tree protection may be more cost effective. These include vole and rabbit guards, plastic mesh and treeshelters (Potter, 1991).

Individual tree protection

Tree shelters are translucent polypropylene tubes which surround the tree, and are kept in position by attachment to wooden stakes. They provide protection from a wide range of predators, and create a favourable microclimate around the tree by acting as a mini-greenhouse. The plastic material is photo degradable and is designed to degrade after about five years. Tree shelters 1.2 m tall were originally intended for use with broadleaved species on fairly sheltered forest sites. They have received little testing on reclaimed mineral sites, but are likely to be blown over on exposed sites. Here, the smaller 0.6 m shelter size is probably the best choice, provided that deer are not a problem.

Voles sometimes pose a threat, particularly where weed control is poor. Well weeded sites suffer less, as voles are reluctant to cross bare ground, but large populations can cause severe tree damage, and even large trees can be killed. Vole guards consist of split plastic tubes which coil around the tree, to a height of between 200 and 300 mm. They should be pushed well into the ground to prevent vole access.

Tending – beating up

Some losses in the first few years after planting are inevitable, and it is not worth replacing failures unless substantial gaps appear in the plantation or the stocking density is less than about 80%. If replacements are necessary, planting should be carried out as soon as possible after initial planting, because delay will increase the likelihood of vegetation competition and prolong the period of weed control. However, it is important to consider why large scale failures have occurred before replanting; if they are due to inhospitable site conditions, then these should be ameliorated, or tree planting avoided. The open areas thus created can form glades in the developing woodland, and diversity, conservation and amenity value of the site can be increased (Land Capability Consultants, 1989).

Nutrition

Satisfactory tree health and growth depend on the availability of essential nutrients in the soil, or soil-forming materials, being used. However, infertility is commonplace on man-made sites (see Chapter 2), mainly because topsoil materials are in short supply. As a general rule, tree species tolerant of comparative infertility should be chosen (p. 46), but, on some substrates, even these species may suffer from nutrient deficiencies. It may be necessary, therefore, to improve the site nutritionally using fertilisers.

Soil diagnosis

Some guidance on the likelihood of nutrient deficiencies, and hence the need to fertilise, comes from an appreciation of how the site has been restored, and what soil, or soil-forming materials, have been used. For some substrates, it is possible to predict with some confidence a fertiliser requirement; for example, pulverised fuel ash (pfa) is usually deficient in the macronutrients nitrogen and phosphorus. Alternatively, soil samples can be collected and analysed to provide information on nutrient levels.

Guidance on the general principles behind soil surveying and sampling are given in Chapter 3. Sampling intensity will depend on the heterogeneity of the materials used, the precision of information required, and the resources available. If resources are limited, sampling from the upper layers of the soil is the most important, though samples taken throughout the anticipated rooting depth of the trees can provide useful additional information.

Analysis of plant-available nutrients is most useful for evaluating fertiliser requirement. They are usually determined using extractants of various kinds. If phosphorus deficiency is likely, the methods of Bray and Kurtz (1945) are recommended; for potassium, magnesium and calcium, the methods of MAFF (1981) are most commonly used. There are no suitable measures of available nitrogen; analysis of organic carbon and total nitrogen must be used to evaluate the nitrogen status of the soil. Methods are given by Avery and Bascomb (1982). Micronutrient deficiencies are rare except in soil materials of high pH, and analysis to determine their content in the soil is not generally recommended.

Foliar diagnosis

Once tree crops have become established, they should be checked periodically during the growing season for any signs of nutrient deficiency. Symptoms include poor growth rate, reduction in needle or leaf size, yellowing of foliage, premature senescence or leaf loss, and premature flowering on young plants. Examples of characteristic visual symptoms of deficiency are given by Binns *et al.* (1980) and Taylor (1991). Sporadic occurrences on individual trees can be discounted, but widespread symptoms require further investigation. Some of the symptoms can arise from other silvicultural problems such as weed competition, waterlogging, compaction or climatic effects.

If nutrient deficiencies are suspected in tree crops up to 3 or 4 m in height, foliage samples should be collected following the guidelines in Appendix 8. Samples should not be taken from tree crops in the first two years after planting as nutrient levels can still be influenced by previous nursery treatments. An analytical service is provided by the Forestry Authority Research Division, at Alice Holt Research Station (see Appendix 8).

Fertilising

Where nutritional deficiencies have been identified, it will be necessary to consider the most appropriate type of remedial action. It may not be necessary to add fertilisers if, for example, weed competition or waterlogging are responsible. In such cases it is better to relieve the cause of the problem. However, if deficiencies are due to substrate infertility, applying inorganic or organic fertiliser is the quickest and most convenient way of providing relief.

Mineral fertilisers

Types of fertiliser and suitable amounts for forest fertilising are given in Taylor (1991). One application of phosphorus or potassium, at or soon after the time of planting, is usually sufficient for a tree rotation. However, nitrogen is more likely to be required at regular intervals, particularly on sites without topsoil or where more demanding species such as Sitka spruce have been planted.

Previous advice has been for fertiliser not to be applied until three to five years after planting, to allow the development of a root system capable of taking up the added nutrients (e.g. Wilson, 1987). However, recent evidence suggests that moderate, and careful, applications of some fertilisers can benefit tree growth even in the first year of growth (Gilbertson *et al.*, 1987). Early application of fertilisers on sites known to be nutrient deficient may therefore be beneficial.

Application of fertiliser using a mechanical spreader mounted on a tractor, is restricted to the period prior to cultivation. Fertilisers are more usually broadcast by hand, so that the total ground surface between and around the trees is covered. Fertiliser use will almost inevitably lead to vigorous weed growth, and it is vital that weed control is addressed.

Organic fertilisers

Compost wastes, and horse and other animal manures are suitable forms of organic fertiliser, but they are usually not available in sufficient quantities to treat large areas effectively. Alternatively, sewage sludge (see Plate 24) is widely available, and contains useful quantities of nitrogen and phosphorus. The nutrient content of the sludge will vary according to where, and in what form, it is produced, but Table 6.4 gives a rough guide to the amounts of nutrients that occur in typical sludges. Many of the nutrients are in an organic form, and are released more slowly than those in conventional mineral fertilisers. In addition, the organic-matter content of sludge may help to improve soil structure. In fact, tree growth response can be as great as, if not greater than, that achieved using mineral fertilisers (see Figure 6.4).

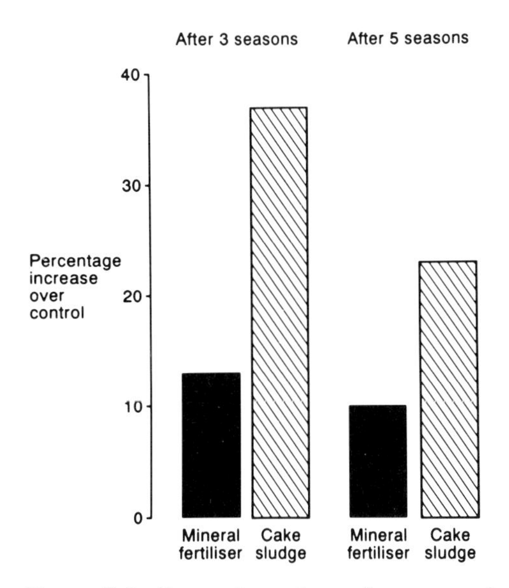

Figure 6.4 Comparison of growth response in Japanese larch to mineral fertiliser and sewage sludge on sandy overburden.

Table 6.4 Typical sewage sludge nutrient analysis

	Total		*Available*[a]	
Sludge type	*N*	*P*	*N*	*P*
Liquid undigested (kg m^{-3})	1.8	0.6	0.6	0.3
Liquid digested (kg m^{-3})	2.0	0.7	1.2	0.3
Undigested cake (kg t^{-1})[b]	7.5	2.8	1.5	1.4
Digested cake (kg t^{-1})	7.5	3.9	1.1	1.9

[a] available in first growing season
[b] wet tonnes

Sludge application to reclamation sites will, in addition to improving tree growth, help to establish a cover of ground vegetation. This may, in some situations, necessitate additional weeding. However, a rapid 'greening' can be very beneficial where the site is easily seen or where the risk of soil erosion is significant.

Using sewage sludge will require greater care than using mineral fertilisers, both in the pre-application planning stages and during the application to the site. *A manual of good practice for the use of sewage sludge in forestry* (Wolstenholme *et al.*, 1992) discusses the safety and environmental aspects of sludge use. It also gives information on consultation procedures, and on legal and health aspects.

Sludge is well known for the heavy metals it can contain. The metal content is very dependent on source; some rural sludges contain relatively low metal concentrations, whilst those affected by industry contain rather more. Some of the metals are, in fact, plant micronutrients and beneficial in small amounts. However, all heavy metals can be toxic if present above critical concentrations. For this reason, the sludge and soil must be analysed before any application, to ensure that maximum permitted soil concentrations of these metals are not exceeded.

Cake sludge, with a higher dry-matter content than liquid sludge, has a consistency similar to compost. It is suitable for applying before cultivation, at rates of up to 100 tonnes dry solids ha^{-1}, though it is important that it is intimately mixed with the substrate it is being applied to. Where there is an existing tree crop, liquid sludge can be applied over the foliage. In order to minimise the risk of water pollution, low application rates, not exceeding 100 m^3 ha^{-1}, should be used until a vegetation cover has become established. It may then be possible to increase this rate to 200 m^3 ha^{-1} as the crop requires further treatment. On land with a slope of between 15° and 25°, the rates suggested above should be halved. No sludge application should be made to land with a slope exceeding 25°, or to soils which suffer prolonged waterlogging.

The risk of water pollution attached to the use of liquid sewage sludges may be reduced if reed bed treatment systems can be installed at appropriate locations along drainage channels or watercourses (Cooper, 1990).

Peat is sometimes considered as an organic 'fertiliser', especially when added to the backfill of pit-planted trees. There appears to be little evidence to support its use in this context (Davies, 1987b), although its retention as a complete soil cover is strongly advocated (p.29).

Section 3 – Reclamation strategies for particular sites

Chapter 7

Derelict land

Introduction

Derelict land is officially defined as:

> 'Land so damaged by industrial or other development that it is incapable of beneficial use without treatment' (Department of the Environment, 1991c).

Most derelict land arising as land spoiled by industrial activity is abandoned due to changes in industrial fortune. It may be affected by a range of special problems not usually met in land worked for minerals, and some of the problems are of importance in its reclamation for forestry. This chapter discusses the most important aspects of derelict land as they affect reclamation to forestry. Most of the reclamation techniques described in Chapters 5 and 6 will be applicable to derelict land reclamation; soil contamination may require additional treatment (p. 59).

Features of derelict land

Poor history

The history of many derelict sites is incomplete, and in some cases little is known about the previous uses of the land. Many sites have been used by a succession of heavy industries; the cumulative effect on the land can be considerable. If records of engineering works and disposal of waste or by-products are poor, substantial exploratory work may be necessary before a site can be deemed to be safe – for humans or for a tree planting scheme.

Site variability

Many derelict sites are associated with old quarrying and mining activities, and the consequent disposal of wastes and overburden materials. The topography of these sites can be complex and severe. Regrading is often necessary before redevelopment, including woodland establishment, can take place.

Soils can be extremely variable on derelict land, especially if materials have been imported from other areas. Soils and wastes can strongly contrast with one another, and this heterogeneity can present difficulties when choosing suitable tree species.

Site instability

Many waste tips are mechanically unstable, especially if slopes are close to the natural angle of repose and sparsely vegetated. Weathering and erosion may act at the surface of the tip material, but poor drainage can cause more deep seated failures. Instability is tackled by attending to drainage and regrading slopes; tree planting can also help increase stability (see Chapter 2). In general, however, tree growth is likely to be improved if slopes are regraded, provided that compaction is not induced during earth-moving operations.

Contamination

The amount of 'potentially contaminated land' in the UK was estimated at about 27 000 ha in 1989, or about 65% of all derelict land (Beckett *et al.*, 1992). Although this figure is unlikely to be strictly accurate, it demonstrates that contamination is probably the norm rather than the exception. Many derelict sites contain a range of toxic materials which can be harmful to animals or plants. Some metallic elements are toxic, but other substances are corrosive or carcinogenic. Table 7.1 gives some guidance on

Table 7.1 Common contaminants and associated industries (from ICRCL, 1987)

Type of contaminant	*Likely to occur on*
Toxic metals, e.g. cadmium, lead, arsenic, mercury Other metals, e.g. copper, nickel, zinc	Metal mines, iron and steel works, foundries, smelters Electroplating, anodising and galvanising works; engineering works, e.g. shipbuilding; scrap yards and car breaking sites
Combustible substances, e.g. coal and coke dust	Gasworks, power stations, railway land
Flammable gases, e.g. methane	Landfill sites, filled dock basins
Aggressive substances, e.g. sulphates, chlorides, acids	Made ground including slags from blast furnaces
Oily and tarry substances, phenols	Chemical works, refineries, by-product plants, tar distilleries
Asbestos	Industrial buildings, waste disposal sites

the type of contamination most usually associated with particular types of industrial activity. Different contaminants pose different hazards depending on the proposed after-uses of the land. For tree planting, heavy metal contents are probably the most important to consider, but other contaminants – such as arsenic, cyanides, polynuclear aromatic hydrocarbons, phenols and sulphates – should also be considered if there is any likelihood of public use of the established woodland (e.g. in community forests where children may play) (British Standards Institution, 1988).

Infertility

Most derelict sites will suffer from a shortage of topsoil; all natural soil materials may be absent. Consequently, plant nutrient deficiencies are common, and may dictate choice of particular tree species and remedial fertiliser additions to promote tree growth.

Poor drainage

This is often upset by previous excavations and tipping activities. Flooding may occur periodically.

Underground hazards

Derelict land usually has dilapidated or ruined buildings on it along with buried structures of brick, concrete, or pipework. These hazards hinder regrading operations and cultivation.

Neighbourhood

Derelict land is often surrounded by a neighbourhood which is run down and under pressure; problems of vandalism are common because there are often few recreational facilities in the area. Derelict land may also be used for fly tipping, motorbike scrambling and other activities which may make tree establishment difficult even after reclamation has taken place.

Survey and assessment of derelict land

It is important to evaluate the potential of a derelict site for tree growth before a planting scheme is commissioned. Information should be obtained in stages which increase in intensity as more is learnt about the site properties which require detailed appraisal. Bridges (1987) gives details of how surveys and assessments should be conducted. A preliminary assessment should take the form of document searching, site visits and some simple laboratory determinations of a small number of soil samples. Specialist surveys may then be needed, and may include surveys of soil resources, contamination, fertility, drainage, hydrogeology and topography. Many more samples may be required for laboratory analysis if, for example, the initial survey reveals areas of severe contamination. Only when the last stage is complete should a reclamation programme be drawn up. The original aims of reclamation may need to be amended if, for example, a shortage of soil materials is identified.

Four main questions must be borne in mind when setting up an investigation of a derelict site where woodland establishment is proposed.

1 Will the site support tree growth?

   Important information to answer this question includes:

   a. the presence/absence/type of phytotoxic contamination;
   b. the levels of fertility/infertility in the soil or wastes;
   c. the amount and physical nature of soil, or suitable soil-forming materials, on site;
   d. site drainage; and
   e. site topography.

2 Will the site still be dangerous after trees have been established?

   Important information to gather includes:
   a. the presence/absence of zootoxic contaminants in the soil or wastes;
   b. the presence/absence of dangerous materials at, or below, the surface;
   c. the presence/absence of lagoons and mine shafts;
   d. slope stability;
   e. erosion risk; and
   f. drainage water quality.

3 Will the growth of trees affect the site adversely?

   Possible problems include:
   a. the uptake of contaminants by tree roots, their movement to the foliage and eventual deposition on the soil surface at leaf-fall;
   b. the acidification of a contaminated substrate by prolonged tree growth, and the consequent increase in contaminant solubility and mobility;
   c. the penetration of capping materials designed to cover and seal contaminated materials or landfill;
   d. windthrow exposing an engineered cap or contaminated materials at the soil surface; and
   e. a mature tree crop, on some substrates, causing slope instability.

4 How will the woodland be managed?

   The initial aims of the woodland establishment will determine how the site should be examined from the viewpoint of woodland management and eventual harvesting. Site drainage and topography are the most important features that affect management operations such as cleaning and thinning.

Contaminated land

Valuable guidance on the identification and investigation of potentially contaminated land is given by the Interdepartmental Committee on the Redevelopment of Contaminated Land (ICRCL, 1987) and the British Standards Institution (1988). Identification of contamination is usually a combination of documentary evidence, visual observation and laboratory analysis of soil or spoil samples. The pattern of vegetation cover can often reveal much about the ability of the soil to support plant growth, and where vegetation is absent for no obvious visual reason, contamination should be suspected and further investigations performed.

Contaminants can be conveniently grouped into two classes: those which are potentially both phytotoxic and zootoxic, and those which are phytotoxic but not normally hazardous to health (ICRCL, 1987). Appendices 9 and 10 present tentative trigger concentrations for some of these contaminants. Some values quoted in Appendix 9 are for parks, playing fields and open space because there are no data for trees. The values given must be interpreted according to type of restoration and site type. Tree planting need not be ruled out if soil concentrations exceed the threshold trigger values, but risk clearly increases with the magnitude of contaminant concentrations above threshold levels. In addition, trigger values are based on soils which are only slightly acidic. On more acidic substrates, and with prolonged growth of some tree species, the toxic effects of some of the contaminants may be increased. The ICRCL (1987) advises that 'professional judgement' must be used when interpreting the results of a contaminant survey.

On heavily contaminated land, where one or more trigger values are grossly exceeded, remedial action may be needed before tree planting can be considered. Four options are possible in practice:

1 excavation of the contaminated soil, for disposal elsewhere, followed where necessary by replacement with clean material;
2 isolation of the contaminated soil by covering it with a suitable thickness of clean inert fill;
3 chemical, biological or physical treatment to destroy or immobilise the contamination; or
4 mixing the contaminated material with clean soil or soil-forming materials to reduce the concentrations to below the threshold trigger values (ICRCL, 1987).

Total removal of contaminated material is very costly, and only permissible to licensed toxic waste disposal sites, which may be a considerable distance away. On-site clean up and processing techniques for contaminated soil are becoming important in some parts of continental Europe (Thornton, 1991), but have not yet been fully tested in the UK. Covering systems are generally the most preferred, using material such as clay, or synthetic liners, to isolate contaminated materials from the soil above them. The interaction between tree roots and covering systems is discussed in Chapter 8.

Derelict land grant

Derelict Land Grant (DLG) is the major source of finance available for reclaiming derelict land. Priority within the DLG programme is given to 'the treatment of land which in its present condition reduces the attractiveness of an area as a place in which to live, work or invest, or because of contamination or other reasons is a threat to public health and safety or the natural environment' (Department of the Environment, 1991c). DLG is now available for reclamation which includes tree planting, for example in community woodlands (Department of the Environment, 1991c). DLG may include approved costs incurred in carrying out a survey of derelict land, '*whether or not reclamation work is subsequently carried out*' (Department of the Environment, 1991c). DLG may also be available for remedial work to deal with the effects of landfill gas arising from closed landfill sites. It is strongly advised that the funding from DLG be explored before any operations concerned with woodland establishment on derelict land are undertaken.

Plates 21 and 22
Effect of legume ground cover:
21. Five year old Sitka spruce on restored opencast coal spoil with indigenous ground vegetation;
22. Similar tree stock in plot sown with *Lotus uliginosus*.

Plate 23 Five year old Sitka spruce on restored opencast spoil in mixture with red alder, Ayrshire.

Plate 24 Application of liquid digested sewage sludge to three year old larch and alder on restored opencast spoils, West Glamorgan.

Plate 25 Effect of landfill gas on trees and ground vegetation.

Plate 26 Alder–ash–cherry mixed woodland over landfill, six years after planting into soil placed by loose tipping.

Chapter 8

Landfill sites

Introduction

Landfilling is the most common form of waste disposal in the UK. It is intimately linked with the minerals industry because most landfilling is into excavations made in the course of mineral working. There are presently some 4200 sites licensed to accept waste in the UK, and up to 6000 sites which have been filled (Knox, 1989). This represents a large body of land – up to 50 000 hectares in total area. Although other forms of waste treatment, such as incineration and recycling, may become more popular in time, landfill is likely to remain the most important throughout the 1990s. Increasingly, restoration of mineral sites to woodland must embrace the possibility that there are landfilling materials beneath the soil cover. In addition, many sites in designated areas of community forests have previously been used for the disposal of wastes of various kinds. It is important, therefore, to appreciate the special problems posed by landfilling, and to identify remedies for their solution well before tree planting takes place.

The landfill environment

Wastes are often classified according to the criteria in Table 8.1. There are few sites where special wastes are disposed of, and most landfill sites receive one or more of the more innocuous forms. Nevertheless, landfilling of any waste materials can lead to environmental problems over and above those normally experienced on man-made sites. The most important of these are discussed here.

Table 8.1 Categories of controlled landfill waste (updated from RMC, 1987)

Waste category	*Description*
Inert waste	Materials derived from the excavation of land which are unaltered from their naturally occurring state; includes brick and concrete waste; sometimes known as clean fill or Class 1 or Class A waste
Household waste	Domestic refuse and civic amenity waste; sometimes known as Class 2 or Class B waste
Commercial waste	Waste arising from shops and offices; sometimes known as Class 3 or Class C waste
Industrial waste	Waste arising from industrial undertakings; sometimes known as Class 4 or Class D waste
Special waste	Includes acids, alkalis, toxic metal compounds and other organic and inorganic compounds such as cyanides and phenols

Landfill gas production

Landfill gas is a complex mixture of gases formed by the decomposition of biodegradable or putrescible wastes (see Table 8.2). Its major constituents are usually methane and carbon dioxide, though other gases can be important, for example hydrogen sulphide. Landfill gas can be produced for several decades in landfills which contain putrescible wastes (Department of the Environment, 1991d). Methane, usually the largest component, is not toxic to plants (Flower *et al.*, 1981), but it acts detrimentally by driving oxygen from the

Table 8.2 Typical landfill gas composition (from Department of the Environment, 1991d)

Component	*Typical value (% volume)*	*Observed maximum (% volume)*
Methane	63.8	88.0
Carbon dioxide	33.6	89.3
Oxygen	0.16	20.9
Nitrogen	2.4	87.0
Hydrogen	0.05	21.1
Carbon monoxide	0.001	0.09
Ethane	0.005	0.014
Ethene	0.018	–
Acetaldehyde	0.005	–
Propane	0.002	0.017
Butanes	0.003	0.023
Higher alkanes	<0.05	0.07
Unsaturated hydrocarbons	0.009	0.048
Halogenated compounds	0.00002	0.032
Hydrogen sulphide	0.00002	35.0
Organosulphur compounds	0.00001	0.028
Alcohols	0.00001	0.127
Others	0.00005	0.023

root zone. However, other gaseous components such as carbon dioxide, ethylene and hydrogen sulphide are toxic, and can severely affect tree health if above critical levels (Dobson and Moffat, 1993) (see Plate 25).

Leachate production

Leachate is the aqueous component which forms within the body of the landfill as a result of water ingress and reaction with putrescible materials. All domestic and most industrial wastes will produce leachate. Table 8.3 gives the typical composition of leachate from a domestic waste landfill site.

A major concern about reclaiming a landfill site for a woodland after-use rests on the possible increase in leachate production brought about by the presence of trees. Such concerns have centred around the perception that tree roots can cause preferential pathways for the ingress of rain water into a landfill, thereby increasing leachate volume (Department of the Environment, 1986). Dobson and Moffat (1993) have recently reviewed the likelihood of this occurring, and conclude that there is probably little cause for concern on modern sites which are engineered to modern standards.

Table 8.3 Typical composition of leachate from a recent domestic landfill site (from Department of the Environment, 1986)

Determinand	*Concentration ($mg\ l^{-1}$, except pH)*
pH	6.2
COD (chemical oxygen demand)	23 800
BOD (biological oxygen demand)	11 900
TOC (total organic carbon)	8000
Fatty acids (as carbon)	5688
Ammoniacal N	790
Oxidised N	3
o-Phosphate	0.73
Chloride	1315
Sodium	960
Magnesium	252
Potassium	780
Calcium	1820
Manganese	27
Iron	540
Nickel	0.6
Copper	0.12
Zinc	21.5
Lead	8.4

Leachate pollution in the soil is comparatively rare on modern landfill sites, and, if it occurs at all, is usually confined to areas around the edge. The chemical nature of leachate can cause toxic symptoms in trees, if taken up, but the main effect is probably one of soil anaerobism because of the large oxygen demand (see Table 8.3).

Elevated temperatures

The microbial decomposition of wastes within the landfill is associated with the emission of energy as heat. As a result, landfill sites are often hotter than unfilled mineral sites. Temperatures as high as 60°C have been recorded within the landfill, but 30 to 40°C are probably more typical (Christensen and Kjeldsen, 1989). Temperatures at the soil surface depend on the thickness of soil cover over the waste (Moffat and Houston, 1991) but, where cover is thin, temperatures over 40°C can occur. Nevertheless, research at Pitsea landfill site in Essex suggested that temperature can be attenuated by the provision of suitable soil cover thickness.

It has been suggested that the heat generated within landfill sites can be directly detrimental to tree health (Wilson, 1991), and indirectly harmful by drying out the overlying soil and reducing its plant-available water content (Binns and Fourt, 1983). However, Moffat and Houston (1991) found that elevated temperatures are associated with increased rather than smaller soil moisture contents, due to an upward movement of water from within the landfill across a temperature gradient (Ruark *et al.*, 1983). Dobson and Moffat (1993) also demonstrated that slightly elevated temperatures are likely to stimulate rather than inhibit tree growth.

Settlement

All landfill sites undergo some settlement, but the degree is determined primarily by type of waste, thickness of landfill, and extent of compacting operations while landfilling takes place. Overall settlement of well compacted waste may be in the order of 10%, but poorly compacted waste may have rates of settlement between 20 and 30% (RMC, 1987). In a deep landfill, this amount of settlement may mean that suitable surcharging is needed before capping takes place. However, differential settlement leading to depressions and hollows is common, making it difficult to plan woodland planting.

Woodland establishment on landfill sites

Recommended practices for woodland establishment on landfill sites have recently been reviewed for the Department of the Environment by Dobson and Moffat (1993). Their proposals are summarised here. They are subdivided into practices relevant to the separate phases of restoration, aftercare and management (5+ years).

Restoration

Operations in the restoration phase include the creation of the final landform, installation of the landfill cap and other pollution control measures, and placement of soil or soil-forming materials.

The landfill landform should be designed to encourage the shedding of surface water so that soil waterlogging and ingress of water into the landfill is minimised. Minimum gradients of 5.5 to 6.0° are suggested, in line with current recommendations for reclaimed mineral sites (see Chapter 5). On long slopes, soil erosion can be prevented by installing contour berms every 20 to 30 m.

A landfill cap is an essential element in pollution control; it serves to reduce water infiltration of waste and thereby minimises leachate generation (Department of the Environment, 1986). The cap also protects the trees planted above it from landfill gas. If made of mineral material, the cap should be well compacted, with a bulk density in the region of 1.8 to 1.9 g cm^{-3}, and a permeability no greater than 1×10^{-7} cm s^{-1} (Department of the Environment, 1986). Clay materials are usually employed in cap construction, but some artificial lining materials, such as high density polyethylene (HDPE) are also used.

Modern landfill sites employ gas control measures, including gas collection beneath the landfill cap and active or passive venting. Such systems are important if tree planting is to take place, because the ingress of landfill gas to the tree root zone will be minimised.

An adequate thickness of rootable soil, or soil-forming material, is as important for the restoration of landfill sites as it is for unfilled mineral sites. To reduce the risk of tree roots extending into the landfill cap beneath the soil cover, Dobson and Moffat (1993) recommend a thickness of 1.5 m. The soil should be placed sensitively, and loose tipping is recommended (see Chapter 5). Soil materials should meet the minimum standards set out in Table 3.2.

Aftercare

The aftercare phase includes cultivation, planting and – as necessary – fertilising, weed control and protection from animals. In most respects, aftercare operations differ little from those needed in conventional reclamation of mineral workings. The main difference lies in the timing of planting.

Where considerable settlement is expected, remedial filling will often be necessary. It is important that the five year aftercare period does not begin until all the restoration activities have been completed (Dobson and Moffat, 1993). It may be prudent, therefore, to delay tree planting until after the majority of settlement and remedial works. In the interim, restoration to a temporary after-use such as grassland would be necessary. It is recommended that conditions specifying an extended management period should be included as part of new planning permissions. These would cover interim restoration, prior to the formal aftercare period when trees would be planted.

Dobson and Moffat (1993) recommend that most tree species that are suitable for man-made sites (see Table 6.3) will tolerate soil conditions on a well restored landfill site (see Plate 26). However, on sites which have a large windthrow hazard, it may be sensible to choose species with a relatively short mature form, to reduce the risk of cap exposure if trees are windthrown. Coppice may be an alternative management strategy in windy areas.

Management

All woodlands require some management. However, the main additional operation suggested for woodlands on modern landfill sites is the monitoring of root growth. Until more is known about the actual behaviour of tree roots, Dobson and Moffat (1993) suggest that a few sample trees be examined at five year intervals for the first 20 years to assess whether roots are affecting the integrity of the capping system. However, this recommendation is interim and cautious, and might be rendered redundant as experience of the behaviour of trees on modern landfill sites increases.

Chapter 9

Reclamation of particular substrates

Introduction

Previous chapters have identified problems which commonly afflict mineral, derelict and landfill sites. Mechanisms for dealing with these problems have been put forward in general terms. This Chapter discusses the reclamation of important mineral sites, overburden and waste materials by individual type. To avoid repetition, only those factors which are especially relevant to a particular site type or material will be discussed in detail; previous chapters deal with the factors such as compaction and infertility from which many of the site types suffer.

Colliery spoil

This material remains an important one to reclaim, with real possibilities for tree planting. In 1988, there were nearly 4700 ha of colliery spoil remaining derelict in England, with almost 4400 ha (about 93%) considered to justify reclamation (Department of the Environment, 1991a). A similar scale of need is likely in Wales and Scotland, though no up-to-date information is available.

Colliery spoil consists predominantly of black shales, mudstones, siltstones, seat-earths and sandstones (rarely limestone), together with a variable remaining coal content (Bridges, 1987).

Disposal of colliery spoil produces characteristic tip heaps which are often conical in shape, though may be in the form of large banks along valley sides in regions such as South Wales. A sizeable proportion of the material, especially in Scotland, has been burnt to produce a more stable material, formed into typical reddish brown 'bings'.

The following is a list of the particular problems presented by colliery spoil.

- Acidity – severe acidity is common in some parts of the UK, and is associated with the oxidation of the mineral pyrites, or iron sulphide, a common constituent of coal spoil. When this mineral is exposed to air and water it oxidises and spoil pH may fall to below 2, with disastrous effects on trees planted in the spoil. Jobling and Stevens (1980) give a fuller account of the processes involved. See overpage for more details.
- Salinity – some spoils, especially those in north east England, may have a large soluble salt content. Where evaporation exceeds rainfall, these salts are carried towards the soil surface, where they accumulate. Severe salinity can result, which may affect the survival and vigour of newly planted trees (Jobling and Stevens, 1980).
- Infertility – colliery spoil usually lacks topsoil, and deficiencies of macronutrients are common. Despite there being moderate levels of nitrogen in colliery spoil, very little is available for plant uptake (Palmer *et al.*, 1985).
- Slope – before regrading, colliery spoil mounds may have slopes of up to 35°. These slopes are often unstable, erodible and difficult to cultivate.
- Compaction – regraded spoil mounds are often deliberately compacted, to exclude air and reduce the risk of spontaneous combustion. Such compaction is incompatible with tree establishment and growth.
- Extreme temperature – the black colour of many colliery spoils can lead to high tem-

peratures during periods of sunshine (p.34).

- Vandalism – most areas of colliery spoil are classified as urban in location (Department of the Environment, 1991a). Vandalism is likely to be a problem in many of these areas, as it has been for previous tree planting on colliery spoil (Jobling and Stevens, 1980).

Acidity

Acidity is the main additional problem posed by some colliery spoils, in terms of both the vegetation established on the spoil and water draining from the site; the latter may threaten potable water supplies. If pyritic material has been used as a final cover, its presence usually shows as bare patches of spoil if the site is vegetated. Ochreous precipitation on the edge of drains or streams draining the site is another clear sign that pyrites is present. However, it may be present even if these symptoms do not occur – in a non-oxidised state.

The best way of dealing with acidity caused by pyrites oxidation is to avoid the placement of pyritic spoil as a final cover. Pyritic material should be identified through a sampling programme, followed by laboratory determination of potential acidity, i.e. a measure of the acid-producing power of the spoil if pyrites is present. There are many methods of determining the pyrite content of a spoil (Dacey and Colbourn, 1979); a useful one based on partial oxidation with nitric acid is given by Colbourn (1980) (see Appendix 11). Even small amounts of pyrite (0.5%) may cause acidity problems, and material containing greater than 0.5% should be rejected wherever possible.

A number of methods exist for treating the acidifying effect of pyrite oxidation (Pulford, 1991). These include barrier methods, which attempt to isolate pyritic material from oxygen and water, or the use of materials which themselves demand oxygen, such as sewage sludge. These methods are either costly or inappropriate for the growth of trees, and the commonest method, using lime to neutralise the acidity, is the most appropriate. Colbourn's (1980) method should be used to determine the amount of lime required, taking full account of the need to neutralise deep into the expected root zone of the tree crop. For example, for each 1% of pyrite in a thickness of 15 cm of spoil, 40 tonnes of limestone per hectare are required to neutralise the potential acidity (Costigan *et al.*, 1981). If the trees are expected to root to a depth of 100 cm, this means applying over 250 tonnes per hectare for each 1% pyrite. Amounts calculated to neutralise surface acidity only will restrict tree rooting to surface zones, and moisture stress and premature windblow will be likely as the trees mature. In addition, rates higher than 100 tonnes per hectare will induce an imbalance in the calcium/magnesium ratio of the spoil, and restrict uptake of phosphorus (Costigan *et al.*, 1982). Hence, large requirements for lime may effectively eliminate tree planting as a worthwhile enterprise.

Opencast coal spoil

Opencast mining began in 1942 as a wartime expedient, and after the war steadily increased in importance as a means of extracting coal. In 1987, nearly 16 million tonnes of coal (16% of total UK production) were obtained by opencast methods in the UK (British Geological Survey, 1989). In 1988, nearly 8500 ha were permitted for the working of opencast coal in England (Department of the Environment, 1991b). A typical site covers an area of 200 hectares. The average overburden to coal ratio is 18 to 1, though up to 40 tonnes of overburden might be moved in parts of some sites to win one tonne of coal. The average life of a UK opencast coal site is five years (British Coal Opencast, 1991).

Opencast coal sites vary considerably in the kinds of problems which must be faced during their restoration and aftercare.

- Unsuitable soil – where opencast coal mining takes place on land previously under agriculture or forestry, soils can potentially be saved for replacement after coaling ceases. However, soils on many areas where opencasting takes place (especially in South Wales and Scotland) are predominantly formed in carboniferous shales, mudstones and clays, or Quaternary drifts derived from these lithologies. Most are clayey, and some are overlain by peat. The soils are therefore slowly permeable and seasonally waterlogged, and are difficult to strip, store and replace without causing damage to soil structure.

- Lack of soil – many opencast sites include areas where previous industry (including deep coal mining) has left the land derelict or contaminated. In the last 20 years, some 6600 ha of derelict land have been worked for opencast coal (British Coal Opencast, 1991). Other land has been repeatedly worked by opencast methods, with deeper seams extracted as technology and economics have dictated. All these kinds of land are likely to suffer a shortage in soil resources.
- Adverse climate – some opencast coal sites, especially in South Wales and Scotland, are at relatively high altitude. They suffer from exposure and have a large annual precipitation – levels of over 1600 mm are common at sites in Ayrshire, and over 2000 mm in parts of West Glamorgan. Many sites in South Wales are classified as exposed (Bendelow and Hartnup, 1980), and many in Scotland occur on land classified as having limited flexibility for the growth and management of tree crops (Macaulay Land Use Research Institute, 1988), principally because of adverse climate and poor soil conditions.
- Adverse overburden characteristics – Carboniferous shales, the most common overburden lithology, will support tree growth but they are inherently infertile, lacking almost any plant available nitrogen, and with little available phosphorus in some regions. In South Wales, shales often have alkaline reaction – with pH as high as 8.6 in places, large concentrations of magnesium, and deficient levels of some micronutrients such as iron, zinc and boron (Bending *et al.*, 1991). Shaly spoils are characterized by their stoniness, their poor available water capacity, and their tendency to compaction.

Reclamation strategy

Because opencast coal sites present such a cocktail of problems for tree establishment and maintenance of growth, they demand very high standards in restoration and aftercare. Choice of soil-forming material, proper soil movements, cultivation, species choice and silvicultural care are especially important.

Choice of soil-forming material

Because, on opencast sites, coal is extracted from an average depth of over 80 metres, and may be recovered from several seams, there are usually opportunities to select overburden materials which are suitable as soil-forming materials. Guidelines for the examination and testing of overburden materials are given in Chapter 3.

Soil movements

On sites where soils are present, soil resource surveys before coaling begins are essential to determine the amount and type of soils present. Especial care is needed in the movement of clayey and peaty soils. Placement using loose-tipping techniques (see Chapter 5) is the most satisfactory where dry soil conditions are difficult to ensure (Duncan and Bransden, 1986), especially in areas of high rainfall (p. 15). In Scotland, peat has been successfully loose tipped to a depth of 1 m in contoured mineral bunds 30 to 40 m wide at the Benbain restored opencast coal site in Ayrshire.

Cultivation

If soils or soil-forming materials must be moved using boxscrapers, or otherwise be damaged through trafficking and mishandling, cultivation must be used to relieve compaction and prepare the site for tree planting. Opencast coal overburdens are notoriously stony, and conventional cultivation equipment may not be adequate. Specialised machinery has been developed to meet the rigours of opencast sites (Wright, 1989). On less stony substrates, heavy duty tines and winged tines (see Chapter 6) can be effective in relieving compaction.

Species choice

Choice of tree species will be determined largely by whether soil is available on site; if, alternatively, trees are to be planted on soil-forming materials, only a restricted range will be suitable (see Table 6.2).

Silviculture

On exposed sites, small plant stock is desirable; large stock is likely to 'socket', and the lower stem will abrade on the coarse spoil. Alder stock must be nodulated to ensure nitrogen-fixing capabilities. Recent research on reclaimed opencast coal sites demonstrates the advantage in height growth conferred by the presence of nodules at tree planting (McNeill *et al.*, 1989).

Conifers show good response to sewage sludge applications on opencast coal spoils (Bayes and Taylor, 1988; Moffat *et al.*, 1991). Sewage sludge, containing useful amounts of nitrogen and phosphorus, is an ideal fertiliser in several ways. It provides the two nutrients which are in shortest supply in coal spoils; it also encourages the growth of a ground vegetation, which helps to prevent erosion, promote soil formation, and improve the appearance of the spoil until canopy closure. Figure 9.1 shows the response of Japanese larch to sewage sludge at the Tredeg restored opencast coal site, where shales and sandstones were used as soil-forming materials.

Sand and gravel workings

Sand and gravel (excluding specialised sands such as silica sand) are the minerals most extensively worked in England. In 1988, over 29 000 ha were permitted for their extraction (Department of the Environment, 1991b), and in 1987 over 82 million tonnes were produced. In contrast, only a little over 3 million tonnes were produced in Scotland and less than 3 million tonnes in Wales (British Geological Survey, 1989). The majority of the mineral worked is from surface or near-surface deposits of Quaternary age. Many are located along river valleys or on old plateau terraces. Prominent sand and gravel working has taken place in the Thames, Severn and Trent valleys.

Between 1982 and 1988, almost 60% of the land reclaimed in England from mineral workings to forestry use was in southern England, mainly where plateau gravels were extracted from Bramshill Forest. Considerable research has taken place there since the 1970s in order to improve tree establishment and growth. These are the main factors identified.

- Level or very gently sloping terrain – restoration without the introduction of shallow slopes (p. 14) can lead to drainage problems.
- High water table – this is likely where gravels are extracted from river terraces close to the river floodplain. The ridge and furrow landform (p. 33) can be valuable in maximising the area of land unaffected by waterlogging.
- Stoniness of overburden materials – the available water capacity of many overburden materials is low, and droughtiness is common.
- Susceptibility to compaction – soils and overburden materials are very susceptible to compaction. Bulk densities as high as 2.0 g cm^{-3} have been recorded after soil replacement at Bramshill Forest (Moffat and Roberts, 1989c).
- Acidity and infertility – materials used in the restoration of sand and gravel sites on plateau gravels are usually acidic – pH c. 4. Phosphorus deficiencies are also common (Fourt and Best, 1983).

Reclamation strategy

The factors just summarised have influenced a reclamation policy for former sand and gravel workings which is very successful. The ridge and furrow landform has been widely

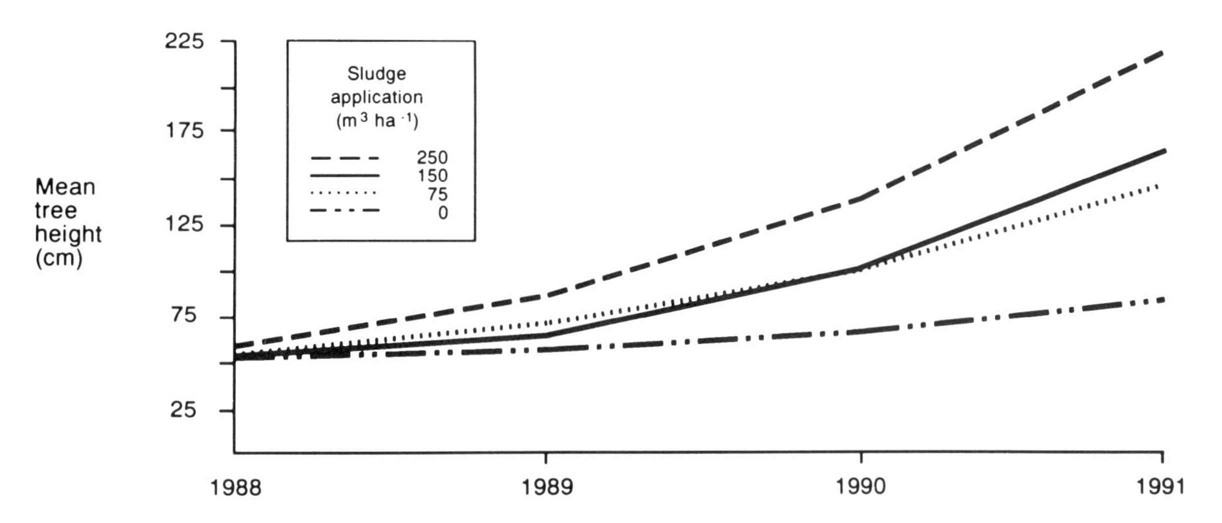

Figure 9.1 Response of Japanese larch to liquid sewage sludge on opencast coal spoils in South Wales.

employed, with cross ripping to 0.5 or 0.75 m depth to relieve compaction (p.33). Pines, predominantly Corsican pine, have been chosen as most suitable for the soil materials present. Yield classes of between 12 and 14 have been obtained for Corsican pine grown on restored workings in Bramshill Forest. Douglas fir may also be suitable on moderately fertile sites where deer control can be exercised. There is increasing interest in the use of loose tipping in the restoration of sand and gravel workings, and preliminary results suggest that this method of soil placement can do much to reduce compaction, and eliminate the need to cultivate.

China clay spoil

China clay extraction is an important industry in south-west England; after oil, china clay is the most valuable of the UK's raw material exports. Over 3 million tonnes were sold in 1987 (British Geological Survey, 1989). However, for every one tonne of clay extracted, seven tonnes of waste are produced (Anon, 1987). Most of this waste is dumped in large tips – especially in the area around St. Austell, where they form impressive but incongruous features in the landscape. Other disposal areas are on Bodmin Moor and Dartmoor. In 1988, over 4000 ha were permitted for spoil disposal (Department of the Environment, 1991b). Tips vary in size but the largest are over 100 m high. The majority of the china clay waste materials consists of gritty coarse sand, with 30 to 50% stones >2mm, and less than 5% silt and clay. The stones are mainly quartz; other mineral constituents include feldspar and mica, but in small amounts. Other wastes include mica, usually disposed of in lagoons, overburden and 'stent' (waste rock).

Particular problems presented by china clay spoil for tree establishment and growth are listed here.

- Slope – sand tip slopes are usually steep – up to 35°, the natural angle of repose for the waste. Some slopes are unstable, and sand moves continuously downwards under the influence of gravity, wind and rain (Sheldon and Bradshaw, 1977). Steep slopes hinder planting, and instability may lead to burial of some trees and exposure of roots in others. Ground vegetation establishment is essential to minimise these problems. Eventual tree harvesting is likely to be costly, and probably uneconomic; the objectives of woodland establishment on these spoils should not include timber production.
- Altitude and exposure – most spoil tips in the St. Austell area occur above 160 m OD, and

many rise to over 200 m OD. The tips usually form the highest land in the region, and are very exposed. Altitude also strongly influences temperature and effective rainfall.

- Infertility – the predominantly quartzose nature of the spoil provides few plant nutrients, and deficiencies of nitrogen, phosphorus and base nutrients are likely. There is no significant organic matter content. It is difficult to counter infertility by adding fertilisers, because leaching losses of all macronutrients are high (Marrs and Bradshaw, 1980).
- Acidity – china clay wastes are naturally very acidic; pH values of 3.9 to 4.8 are common in untreated wastes (Bradshaw *et al.*, 1975). Liming is a common practice over many of the tips, to increase pH to around 6.5 and promote grass growth (Anon, 1987). However, repeated liming is necessary, and may be difficult to perform on tree planted areas.
- Moisture supply – the coarse nature of the waste material restricts water retention after rainfall, and the available water content is small – only 70 mm in one metre of material at Littlejohns tip (Moffat and Roberts, 1989b). However, moisture deficits are not acute in these areas of high rainfall, and moisture stress is only likely to be a sporadic problem. Nevertheless, weed control is vital in the period of tree establishment.

Reclamation strategy

Recent experimental tree planting has shown that trees can be established on china clay wastes, despite the problems just summarised (Moffat and Roberts, 1989b). The most successful tree species are those tolerant of exposure, acidity and relative infertility – namely Sitka spruce, Corsican pine and alders, particularly green and Italian alders. Mixed plantations of pine and green alder at 1.4 m spacing have been the most successful on exposed sites. On more sheltered areas, both Italian and green alders have led to an increase in the height of pine compared with pure pine plots (see Table 9.1). The height response is due both to a shelter effect and to a nutritional benefit from the nitrogen fixed by the alder component. Other species which have shown some promise on less exposed slopes include larch, Scots pine and Monterey pine.

Table 9.1 Effect of alder on growth of Corsican pine, Littlejohn's tip, Cornwall

Treatment	*Height after 6 growing seasons (cm)*	*Percentage increase over control*
2m spacing between pines, 1.4 m spacing between pine and alder		
Control (pure pine)	92	–
Pine in Italian alder	136	48
Pine in green alder	124	35
2 m spacing between all trees		
Control (pure pine)	92	–
Pine in Italian alder	125	37
Pine in green alder	127	40

Nitrogen-fixing shrubs may also help in early tree establishment. Tree lupin (*Lupinus arboreus*) is particularly successful on china clay wastes (Palaniappan *et al.*, 1979), and can add nitrogen to the site at rates of about 180 kg ha^{-1} yr^{-1}. Everlasting pea (*Lathyrus sylvestris*) is another successful coloniser, and both legumes can enhance the growth of some tree species planted amongst them. Like alders, these legumes can donate useful amounts of nitrogen to the tree, and also provide shelter. Palaniappan *et al.* (1979) considered that the best time for tree planting is in the third year of legume growth, when nitrogen availability is optimum. Other nurse plants which have been used to improve the nitrogen capital of china clay spoils include gorse, broom and sea buckthorn. The revegetation of china clay spoils is discussed in detail by Wardell Armstrong (1993).

Metalliferous mine wastes

Non-ferrous metalliferous mining usually creates mine waste tips which contain concentrations of metals that are phytotoxic to some plant types. Similar wastes may also be produced during the extraction and processing of materials such as fluorspar and barytes (Department of the Environment, 1989). In 1988, over 4700 ha of metalliferous spoil heaps were considered derelict in England (Department of the Environment, 1991a), but it has been estimated that over 4000 km^2 of land in England and Wales have been affected by metalliferous mining activities since they began in the Bronze Age (Thornton, 1980). Metalliferous mining is concentrated in certain areas of Britain, especially Cornwall, Derbyshire, the Lake District, and North and Mid Wales.

Metalliferous spoils vary considerably in their physical and chemical properties. Johnson *et al.* (1978) found five major categories of waste materials in a survey of Welsh spoils:

1 mine tailings, enclosed by settlement dams – these consist of fine grained (silt and clay) materials with high residual concentrations of certain metals;

2 intermediate spoils, occurring as conical tips, banks and amorphous heaps – the material is predominantly of sand and grit sized particles (0.02 to 5 mm);

3 coarse grained wastes (5 to 150 mm), comprising fragments of rock and low grade ores – spoil in this category is normally the dominant site material, and distributed throughout the mine workings in relatively stable tips of non-uniform size and shape;

4 coarse grained wastes (20 to 300 mm), consisting of unmineralised rock in hillocks and banks usually around the perimeter of the workings; and

5 metal-contaminated fuel ash and smelting slag, derived from secondary refining of concentrates in simple open hearth and local reverberatory furnaces.

The main problems associated with metalliferous mine wastes include the following:

- Phytotoxicity – high concentrations of non-ferrous metals are common, especially in the mine tailings, but also in the intermediate and some coarse grained wastes.
- Physical nature – the fine grained character of some mine tailings make them susceptible to windblow when dry and to water erosion.
- pH – this may vary from 2 to 8, depending on rock type.
- Infertility – nitrogen is usually lacking in these spoils.
- Animal browsing – rabbits and sheep can be particularly difficult to control in some areas of metalliferous workings.

The non-ferrous metal content of some of the waste types is probably the feature most specific to them: in tailings in Wales, metal contents of up to 2% are common, and very high concentrations of metals can be found in undisturbed spoil heaps and around ore dressing areas (Palmer, 1991). Metal contents are often above phytotoxic levels. Elements most commonly associated with metalliferous mine wastes include copper, zinc, lead, cadmium and arsenic.

The existence of specific heavy-metal-tolerant races in trees has yet to be conclusively demonstrated (Bradshaw, 1981), although there are some indications that distinct ecotypes do occur in some species exposed to large concentrations of some metals (Eltrop *et al.*, 1991). Nevertheless, heavy metal tolerant nursery stock is not yet available, so reclamation is necessary if metal concentrations are above phytotoxic levels. The principle ways in which reclamation can proceed include covering the waste with uncontaminated material, amelioration of the wastes, removal of spoil to a disposal site, and on-site decontamination.

Reclamation strategy

To date, the most common method for reclaiming metalliferous spoils has been their burial under specially constructed covers in order to separate plant roots from toxic soil solutions. Coarse grained materials have often been used, to provide a capillary break and prevent the upward migration of metals. In recent times, there have been moves to cover spoil materials with an impermeable layer, in order to reduce the amount of polluted water that drains from the wastes. Polyethylene membranes, or caps formed with a bentonite mixture, are commonly employed (Palmer, 1991). Soils placed over the membrane must be thick enough to support tree growth, and the final slopes must be shallow enough to prevent slippage. Although soil thicknesses of 50 cm are probably adequate for most occurrences of metalliferous spoils in the UK, it is generally recommended that at least 1 m of rootable soil is placed over the impermeable cap.

Trees have seldom been planted on metalliferous spoils in the UK. However, large numbers of trees were planted on soils contaminated by copper and zinc during the reclamation of the Lower Swansea Valley in the 1960s (Hilton, 1967; Lavender, 1981). More recently, old copper workings in Cornwall have been planted; growth of Scots pine, alders, Sitka spruce, rowan and oak appears to be the most satisfactory (Walker, 1981). There seems to be no reason why woodland cannot be established more widely on some types of metalliferous spoil, particularly the copper/arsenic spoils of Cornwall or the fluorspar spoils of Derbyshire.

Hard rock quarries

Hard rock quarries are particular forms of mineral workings where there is usually very little overburden or spoil. Such quarries principally provide igneous rock, limestone/dolomite, sandstone and some vein minerals. In England, over 22 000 ha were actively affected by these forms of mining in 1988 (Department of the Environment, 1991b). Together, the UK production of these minerals (except vein minerals) was nearly 190 million tonnes in 1987 (British Geological Survey, 1989).

The quarries are usually worked by blasting and are often very deep. They may have shear backwalls, but are more often worked in a series of lifts, forming benches of approximately 15 to 20 m in height and 10 to 15 m in width. Bench faces range from 70-90° and overall slopes from 45-60° (Land Use Consultants, 1992).

Reclamation strategy

Opportunities for restoring hard rock quarries to a woodland after-use are limited by landform and lack of soil materials. It is usually impractical to consider importing materials specifically for restoration purposes, though some quarries are used for the disposal of waste of various kinds (see Chapter 8). Areas where tree planting may be possible include the quarry floor, scree and talus slopes, and the sequential rock benches on the backwall. However, provision must be made for adequate thicknesses of rootable soil materials on these sites.

Restoration blasting (see Chapter 5) can be used effectively to increase the amount of scree material, though subsequent tree survival may depend on whether this technique can generate sufficient finer materials to supply plant-available moisture. Alternatively, crushed materials can be used to dress coarser ones and provide a suitable substrate for vegetation establishment (Bailey and Gunn, 1991). If soil and overburden materials are present in sufficient amounts, substrates suitable for tree planting can also be achieved by pushing them over the face of the quarry, to rest on the benches or form scree slopes at its base. Depending on the lithology of the rock quarried, and the presence of the water table, it may be possible to rip the quarry floor to provide a suitable substrate for tree planting.

The tree species chosen for planting will depend on the chemical nature of the soil or spoil material used. However, where raw rock wastes are used, choice is likely to be very restricted, and limited to species able to tolerate drought. On limestone and chalk lithologies, soil pH is high, and base tolerant species must be chosen. Table 6.2 gives guidance on species choice. The revegetation of hard rock quarries is discussed in detail by Land Use Consultants (1992).

Pulverised fuel ash

The majority of thermal power stations in the UK burn coal which is pulverised so that 80% passes a 200-mesh sieve (aperture 0.07 mm). It is then fluidized in a hot air stream and passed through a burner where it is combusted. Up to 97% of the carbon in the coal is oxidised during this process. The ash from the coal burning is either removed by mechanical and electrostatic precipitators, for dry disposal, or converted into an aqueous slurry, for transport via pipeline to a lagoon. Ash then settles out, and is removed for disposal in large bunds (Townsend and Hodgson, 1973).

Nearly nine million tonnes of pulverised fuel ash (pfa) are produced each year in the UK (Arup Economics, 1991). Four million tonnes are used in the construction industry, but much of the remainder requires disposal in lagoons and mounds adjoining the power stations that produce the material.

Pfa is predominantly silt or fine sand in size, and consists of discrete white or colourless glassy spherical particles. It presents some unusual properties which affect tree establishment and growth.

- pH – alkalinities of pH 11 or 12 are common in fresh pfa, but lagooned pfa more often develops a pH between 8 and 9 (Townsend and Hodgson, 1973). Over time, organic upper layers sometimes form with pH values nearer 7, though these layers are usually thin.
- Infertility – Table 9.2 shows mean values (and ranges) for plant nutrients from a wide range of pfa samples. There is an almost complete lack of nitrogen, though levels of other nutrients may be adequate for tree growth.

Table 9.2 Mean nutrient content of pfa, range in parentheses (from Cope, 1961)

Nutrient	*Total*	*Available*	
Nitrogen	0.04%	na	
Phosphorus	0.05%	0.01%	(0.01–0.02)
Potassium	2.23%	0.04%	(0.01–0.10)
Calcium	4.69%	0.99%	(0.28–1.87)
Magnesium	0.71%	0.15%	(0.01–0.52)
Iron	0.09%	0.06%	(0.00–0.23)
Sulphur	0.48%	0.39%	(0.07–0.55)
Manganese	848ppm	99ppm	(12–347)
Boron	236ppm	43ppm	(10–50)
Zinc	283ppm	2.1ppm	(0–4)
Copper	248ppm	25ppm	(10–50)
Molybdenum	42ppm	5.4ppm	(0.7–12.8)

- Toxicity – pfa is well known for its high concentration of boron. Concentration of water-soluble boron ranges from 3 to 250 ppm, with a mean of about 60 ppm (Cope, 1961). Weathering gradually reduces boron content, though it usually remains above toxic levels for many years. Other soluble salts lead to high electrical conductivities; values measured on fresh pfa may range from 0.8 to 1.3 Sm^{-1}, and growth of plants will be restricted. However, unlike boron concentrations, conductivity falls relatively rapidly to safe levels, between two and three years after lagooning.
- Physical properties – pfa laid down in lagoons is typically stratified, and hard and compact layers, from one mm to several cm thick, occur randomly through the sedimentary sequence (Townsend and Hodgson, 1973). The platy structure of the material that results can seriously hinder vertical root penetration. Tree roots tend to grow horizontally, radiating in all directions in the looser surface ash. Poplar roots examined by Hodgson and Buckley (1975) were restricted to the upper 7 or 8 cm, and most were in the upper 3 to 5 cm. Trees with such roots are likely to suffer from drought and instability as they grow taller.

  Another physical problem of pfa deposits is surface erosion (Townsend and Hodgson, 1973). The risk of wind erosion is particularly acute, and dust from lagoon sites can be a considerable nuisance if not controlled. Pfa materials must therefore be seeded to grass or a grass/legume mixture if trees are to be established on them.

Reclamation strategy

These properties of pfa demand that special attention is paid to species choice when planting trees. Table 9.3 lists species according to tolerance to the chemical nature of pfa. Nitrogen-fixing trees and shrubs such as alder, false acacia and oleaster are prominent in the list, but some other species appear to do well, particularly some poplars and willows. Tolerant trees can be established directly in pfa, but growth is likely to be markedly encouraged by the addition of a layer of soil or soil-forming material. For example, Hodgson and Townsend (1973) showed the usefulness of a 15 cm layer of colliery shale or soil mixed into the upper 30 cm of lagooned pfa for a range of tree species. Similarly, Moffat (1991) found that a 20 cm layer of sand over pfa improved the growth of alder and poplar species.

Table 9.3 Tolerance of trees to pfa: a selection of species which have undergone testing (from Hodgson and Townsend, 1973; Hodgson and Buckley, 1975; Moffat, 1991)

Tolerance	*Species*
Tolerant	*Populus nigra* 'Italica'
	Picea sitchensis
	Eleagnus angustifolia
	Populus alba
	Tamarix gallica
	Alnus glutinosa
	Salix spp.
Semi-tolerant	*Alnus cordata*
	Betula pendula
	Pinus nigra var. *maritima*
	Picea omorika
	Ailanthus glandulosa
	Robinia pseudoacacia
Sensitive	*Fagus sylvatica*
	Chamaecyparis lawsoniana
	Fraxinus excelsior
	Acer pseudoplatanus

Deep ripping across a pfa planting site will encourage both root penetration and the leaching of boron and soluble salts. However, rip lines must be closely spaced (no greater than 1 m apart) to ensure complete shattering of compacted ash. The results of ripping can persist for several years, but planting should take place soon after ripping and before ash begins to reconsolidate.

Leguminous plants can also help to improve the fertility of pfa materials, but it is important that strict weed control is adopted around the trees in accordance with current recommendations (see Chapter 6).

FGD gypsum

As part of the UK Government's commitment to reducing atmospheric pollution, certain thermal power stations are being fitted with flue gas desulphurization (FGD) plants in order to reduce SO_2 emissions. The limestone/gypsum system has been chosen for several power stations, involving the use of crushed limestone as an input, with gypsum ($CaS0_4.2H_20$) as the main solid by-product. Large amounts of limestone and gypsum will be involved. For example, at the 4000 MW Drax power stations in West Yorkshire, it is estimated that over 2000 tonnes of high quality gypsum will be produced each day. Some of this material may be sold for plasterboard, but it is likely that considerable quantities will require disposal on land. Lagooning gypsiferous materials is the most probable solution, though co-disposal with pfa is also possible.

Recent research has evaluated the potential of gypsum materials for tree establishment (Moffat, 1991). FGD gypsum is nutritionally almost inert, containing no nitrogen or extractable phosphorus, very little plant available potassium, but sufficient plant available magnesium. It has a pH above 6, a high electrical conductivity, and soluble salt and sulphate contents (Moffat, 1989). These features make it potentially toxic for many plant species, but tree species trials have shown that poplars (*Populus nigra* 'Italica', *P. alba*), alders (*Alnus glutinosa, A. cordata*) and false acacia (*Robinia pseudoacacia*) can grow remarkably well, once essential nutrients have been added (Moffat, 1991). However, the inherent infertility of the gypsum means that fertiliser additions are likely to be needed for a considerable time after tree establishment, until soil organic matter levels have increased to the stage where nutrient cycling is taking place efficiently. Sewage sludge may be an alternative source of nitrogen and phosphorus, though there is, as yet, no direct experience of using sludge on this medium.

Like pfa, FGD gypsum is very susceptible both to capping and crusting, and to erosion. It is important that sites chosen for tree planting are undersown with tolerant ground vegetation species, and that weed control around the trees is good.

REFERENCES

ANDREWS, J. and KINSMAN, D. (1990). *Gravel pit restoration for wildlife*. Royal Society for the Protection of Birds, Sandy.

ANON (1987). Environmental management at English China Clays. *M & Q Environment* **1**, 16–18.

ARUP ECONOMICS (1991). *Occurrence and utilisation of mineral and construction wastes*. HMSO, London.

AVERY, B.W. (1987). Soil survey methods: a review. *Soil Survey and Land Research Centre Technical Monograph 18*. Silsoe.

AVERY, B.W. and BASCOMB, C.L. (1982). Soil survey laboratory methods. *Soil Survey Technical Monograph 6*. Harpenden.

AVERY, M. and LESLIE, R. (1990). *Birds and forestry*. Poyser, London.

BÅÅTH, E. (1989). Effects of heavy metals in soil on microbial processes and populations (a review). *Water, Air and Soil Pollution* **47**, 335–379.

BAILEY, D.E. and GUNN , J. (1991). Landform replication as an approach to the reclamation of limestone quarries. *In:* M.C.R. DAVIES, ed. *Land reclamation. An end to dereliction?* Elsevier Applied Science, London, pp. 96–105.

BAYES, C.D. and TAYLOR, C.M.A. (1988). The use of sewage sludge in the afforestation of former opencast coal sites: Clydesdale Forest Trials. *Water Research Centre Report,* PRU 1774–M/2. Water Research Centre, Medmenham.

BECKETT, M., DOBBS, A.J. and GOURLAY, D. (1992). The impact of contaminated land on freshwater quality. *In: Freshwater quality. Additional reports for the Royal Commission on Environmental Pollution*. HMSO, London.

BENDELOW, V.C. and HARTNUP, R. (1980). Climatic classification of England and Wales. *Soil Survey Technical Monograph 15*. Harpenden.

BENDING, N.A.D., MOFFAT, A.J. and ROBERTS, C.J. (1991). Site factors affecting tree response on restored opencast ground in the South Wales coalfield. *In:* M.C.R. DAVIES, ed. *Land reclamation. An end to dereliction?* Elsevier Applied Science, London, pp. 347–356.

BENGTSSON, G. and TRANVIK, L. (1989). Critical metal concentrations for forest soil invertebrates. *Water, Air and Soil Pollution* **47**, 381–417.

BENSON, J.F. and WILLIS, K.G. (1991). The demand for forests for recreation. *In: Forestry expansion: a study of technical, economic and ecological factors*. Occasional Paper 39. Forestry Commission, Edinburgh.

BEST, N. (1983). Legume supplies. *Report on forest research, Edinburgh 1983*. HMSO, London, p. 20.

BINNS, W.O. (1982). Reclaiming mineral workings for forestry. *Span* **25**, 74–76.

BINNS, W.O. and FOURT, D.F. (1976). Lowland production forestry. Gravel workings. *Report on forest research, London 1976*. HMSO, London, p. 22.

BINNS, W.O. and FOURT, D.F. (1981). Surface workings and trees. *In: Research for practical arboriculture*. Occasional Paper 10. Forestry Commission, Edinburgh, 60–75.

BINNS, W.O. and FOURT, D.F. (1983). Advisory. *Report on forest research, Edinburgh 1983*. HMSO, London, p. 22.

BINNS, W.O., MAYHEAD, G.J. and MACKENZIE, J.M. (1980). *Nutrient deficiencies of conifers in British forests*. Forestry Commission Leaflet 76. HMSO, London.

BRADSHAW, A.D. (1981). Growing trees in difficult environments. *In: Research for practical arboriculture*. Occasional Paper 10. Forestry Commission, Edinburgh, 93–106.

BRADSHAW, A.D., DANCER, W.S., HANDLEY, J.F. and SHELDON, J.C. (1975). The biology of land revegetation and the reclamation of the china clay wastes in Cornwall. *In:* M.J. CHADWICK and G.T. GOODMAN, eds. *The ecology of resource degradation and renewal*. Blackwell, Oxford, pp. 363–384.

BRANSDEN, B.E. (1981). Soil protection as a component of gravel raising. *Soil Use and Management* **7**, 139–145.

BRAY, R.H. and KURTZ, L.T. (1945). Determination of total, organic and available forms of phosphorus in soils. *Soil Science* **59**, 39–45.

BRIDGES, E.M. (1987). *Surveying derelict land.* Clarendon Press, Oxford.

BRITISH COAL OPENCAST (1991). *Opencast coal mining in Great Britain.* British Coal Opencast, Mansfield.

BRITISH GEOLOGICAL SURVEY (1989). *United Kingdom minerals yearbook 1988.* British Geological Survey, Keyworth.

BRITISH STANDARDS INSTITUTION (1980). *Nursery stock. Part 1. Specification for trees and shrubs.* BS3936: Part 1: 1980. British Standards Institution, London.

BRITISH STANDARDS INSTITUTION (1984). *Nursery stock. Part 4. Specification for forest trees.* BS3936: Part 4: 1984. British Standards Institution, London.

BRITISH STANDARDS INSTITUTION (1988). *Code of practice for the identification of potentially contaminated land and its investigation.* British Standards Institution, London.

BRITISH STANDARDS INSTITUTION (1989). *Code of practice for general landscape operations.* BS4428: 1989. British Standards Institution, London.

BROAD, K.F. (1979). *Tree planting on man-made sites in Wales.* Occasional Paper 3. Forestry Commission, Edinburgh.

BUCKLEY, G.P. (1984). The uses of herbaceous companion species in the establishment of woody species from seed. *Journal of Environmental Management* **18**, 309–322.

BURTON, K.W., MORGAN, E. and ROIG, A. (1983). The influence of heavy metals upon the growth of sitka-spruce in South Wales forests. *Plant and Soil* **73**, 327–336.

CHRISTENSEN, T.H. and KJELDSEN, P. (1989). Basic biochemical processes in landfills. *In:* T.H. CHRISTENSEN, R. COSSU and R. STEGMANN, eds. *Sanitary landfilling: process, technology and environmental impact.* Academic Press, London, pp. 29–50.

COLBOURN, P. (1980). Estimation of the potential oxidation rate of pyrite in coal mine spoils. *Reclamation Review* **2**, 113–121.

COMMISSION ON ENERGY AND THE ENVIRONMENT (1981). *Coal and the environment.* HMSO, London.

COOK, D.I. and VAN HAVERBEKE, D.F. (1972). Trees, shrubs and land-forms for noise control. *Journal of Soil and Water Conservation* 27, 259–261.

COOPER, P.F. (Ed.) (1990) European design and operations guidelines for reed bed treatment systems. *WRc Report UI 17.* Medmenham.

COPE, F. (1961). *The agronomic value of power station ash.* Unpublished Ph.D. thesis, University of Leeds.

COPPIN, N.J. and BRADSHAW, A.D. (1982). *Quarry reclamation.* Mining Journal Books Ltd, London.

COPPIN, N.J. and RICHARDS, I.G. (1990). *Use of vegetation in civil engineering.* Butterworths, London.

COPPOCK, R.C. (1986). A comparison of five different types of Corsican pine planting stock at Delamere Forest. *Quarterly Journal of Forestry* **80**, 165–171.

COSTIGAN, P.A., BRADSHAW, A.D. and GEMMELL, R.P. (1981). The reclamation of acidic colliery spoil. I. Acid production potential. *Journal of Applied Ecology* **18**, 865–878.

COSTIGAN, P.A., BRADSHAW, A.D. and GEMMELL, R.P. (1982). The reclamation of acidic colliery spoil. III. Problems associated with the use of high rates of limestone. *Journal of Applied Ecology* **19**, 193–201.

CRAUL, P.J. (1985). A description of urban soils and their desired characteristics. *Journal of Arboriculture* **11**, 330–339.

CUTLER, D.F. (1991). Tree planting for the future: lessons of the storms of October, 1987 and January, 1990. *Arboricultural Journal* **15**, 225–234.

DACEY, P.W. and COLBOURN, P. (1979). An assessment of methods for the determination of iron pyrites in coal mine spoil. *Reclamation Review* **2**, 113–121.

DANIELS, W.L. and AMOS, D.F. (1984). Generating productive topsoil substitutes from hardrock overburden in the Southern Appalachians. *Environmental Geochemistry and Health* **7**, 8–15.

DAVIES, R.J. (1987a). *Trees and Weeds.* Forestry Commission Handbook 2. HMSO, London.

DAVIES, R.J. (1987b). Tree establishment: soil amelioration, plant handling and shoot pruning. *In:* D. PATCH, ed. *Advances in practical arboriculture.* Forestry Commission Bulletin 65. HMSO, London, pp. 52–57.

DAVIS, B.N.K. (1976). Wildlife, urbanisation and industry. *Biological Conservation* **10**, 249–291.

DAWKINS, H.C., HOCKIN, R.L. and POWER, J.D. (1985). First observations of ecological surveillance plots on afforested open-cast spoil in South Wales. *Commonwealth Forestry Institute Occasional Paper No. 25.* Oxford.

DEPARTMENT OF THE ENVIRONMENT (1986). *Landfilling wastes.* Waste Management Paper 26. HMSO, London.

DEPARTMENT OF THE ENVIRONMENT (1988). *Minerals planning guidance: applications, permissions and conditions.* Minerals Planning Guidance Note 2. HMSO, London.

DEPARTMENT OF THE ENVIRONMENT (1989). *Minerals planning guidance: the reclamation of mineral workings.* Minerals Planning Guidance Note 7. HMSO, London.

DEPARTMENT OF THE ENVIRONMENT (1991a). *Survey of derelict land in England, 1988.* HMSO, London.

DEPARTMENT OF THE ENVIRONMENT (1991b). *Survey of land for mineral workings in England, 1988.* HMSO, London.

DEPARTMENT OF THE ENVIRONMENT (1991c). *Derelict land grant policy.* Derelict Land Grant Advice Note 1. HMSO, London.

DEPARTMENT OF THE ENVIRONMENT (1991d). *Landfill gas.* Waste Management Paper 27, HMSO, London.

DOBSON, M.C. and MOFFAT, A.J. (1993). *The potential for woodland establishment on landfill sites.* HMSO, London.

DOWNING, H.F. (1977). Landform design and grading. *In:* B. HACKETT, ed. *Landscape reclamation practice*. IPC Scientific and Technical Press, pp. 85–124.

DUNCAN, N.A. and BRANSDEN, B.E. (1986). The effects on a restored soil caused by soil moving under different moisture contents. *Applied Geography* **6**, 267–273.

EDWARDS, M.V., ATTERSON, J. and HOWELL, R.S. (1963). *Wind loosening of young trees on upland heaths.* Forestry Commission Forest Record 50. HMSO, London.

ELTROP, L., BROWN, G., JOACHIM, O. and BRINKMAN, K. (1991). Lead tolerance of *Betula* and *Salix* in the mining area of Mechernich, Germany. *Plant and Soil* **131**, 275–285.

FARMER, A.M. (1992). The effects of dust on vegetation – a review. *Environmental Pollution* **79**, 63–75.

FARRAR, J.F., RELTON, J. and RUTTER, A.J. (1977). Sulphur dioxide and the scarcity of *Pinus sylvestris* in the industrial Pennines. *Environmental Pollution* **14**, 63–68.

FINEGAN, B.G. (1984). Forest succession. *Nature, London* **312**, 109–114.

FLOWER, F.B., GILMAN, E.F. and LEONE, I.A. (1981). Landfill gas, what it does to trees and how its injurious effects may be prevented. *Journal of Arboriculture* **7**, 43–52.

FORESTRY COMMISSION (1989). *Provisional code of practice for the use of pesticides in forestry.* Occasional Paper 21. Forestry Commission, Edinburgh.

FORESTRY COMMISSION (1990). *Why grow trees? Britain's forests.* Forestry Commission, Edinburgh.

FORESTRY COMMISSION (1991a). *Woodland grant scheme.* Forestry Commission, Edinburgh.

FORESTRY COMMISSION (1991b). *Community woodland design guidelines.* HMSO, London.

FORESTRY COMMISSION (1993). *Forests and water guidelines.* Third Edition. HMSO, London.

FOURNIER, F. (1972). *Soil conservation.* Nature and Environment Series. Council of Europe, Strasbourg.

FOURT, D.F. (1978). Restoration of spoils. *Report on forest research, London 1978.* HMSO, London, p. 24.

FOURT, D.F. (1979). Winged tines and restoration of gravel pits. *Saga Bulletin* **11**, 4, 12.

FOURT. D.F. (1980a). Spoils and nitrogen. *Report on forest research, Edinburgh 1980.* HMSO, London, 24–25.

FOURT, D.F. (1980b). Reclamation methods. *Report on forest research, Edinburgh 1980.* HMSO, London, p. 24.

FOURT, D.F. (1984a). Reclamation: peat-covered sites. *Report on forest research, Edinburgh 1984.* HMSO, London, p. 24.

FOURT, D.F. (1984b). Lowland forestry. Reclamation: machinery. *Report on forest research, Edinburgh 1984.* HMSO, London, p. 22.

FOURT, D.F. and BEST, N. (1981). Open-cast mineral sites – legumes. *Report on forest research, Edinburgh 1981.* HMSO, London, 25–26.

FOURT, D.F. and BEST, N. (1982). Open-cast mineral sites: nitrogen nutrition. *Report on forest research, Edinburgh 1982.* HMSO, London, 17–18.

FOURT, D.F. and BEST, N. (1983). Reclamation: sand and gravel. *Report on forest research, Edinburgh 1983.* HMSO, London, p. 19.

FOURT, D.F. and CARNELL, R. (1979). Gravel workings. *Report on forest research, Edinburgh 1979.* HMSO, London, p. 22.

FROEHLICH, H.A. and McNABB, D.H. (1984). Minimizing soil compaction in Pacific Northwest forests. *In:* E.L. STONE, ed. *Forest soils and treatment impacts. Proceedings of the 6th North American forest soils conference.* University of Tennessee, Tennessee, pp. 159–192.

GAWN, P. (1991). *Landscape architecture: gas monitoring techniques.* Proceedings of a National Association of Waste Disposal Contractors training course on the practical landfill restoration and after-care of landfill sites. Welwyn, 18–19 April 1991.

GEYER, W.A. and ROGERS, N.E. (1972). Spoil changes and tree growth on coal mined spoil in Kansas. *Journal of Soil and Water Conservation* **27**, 114–116.

GILBERT, O.L. (1983). The growth of planted trees subject to fumes from brickworks. *Environmental Pollution Series A* **31**, 301–310.

GILBERTSON, P., KENDLE, A.D. and BRADSHAW, A.D. (1987). Root growth and the problems of trees in urban and industrial areas. *In:* D. PATCH, ed. *Advances in practical arboriculture.* Forestry Commission Bulletin 65. HMSO, London, pp. 59–66.

GILL, C.J. (1970). The flooding tolerance of woody species – a review. *Forestry Abstracts* **31**, 671–688.

GOODMAN, G.T. and ROBERTS, T.M. (1971). Plants and soils as indicators of metals in the air. *Nature, London* **231**, 287–292.

GREACEN, E.L. and SANDS, R. (1980). Compaction of forest soils: a review. *Australian Journal of Soil Research* **18**, 163–189.

GREEN, J.E. and SALTER, R.E. (1987). *Methods for reclamation of wildlife habitat in the Canadian Prairie Rockies.* Environment Canada, Edmonton.

GREENWOOD, E.F. and GEMMELL, R.P. (1978). Derelict industrial land as a habitat for rare plants in S. Lancs (v.c. 59) and W. Lancs (v.c. 60). *Watsonia* **12**, 33–40.

HAIGH, M.J. (1979). Ground retreat and slope evolution on plateau-type colliery spoil mounds at Blaenavon, Gwent. *Transactions of the Institute of British Geographers, New Series* **4**, 321–328.

HALL, R.L. and ROBERTS, J.M. (1990). Hydrological aspects of new broad-leaf plantations. *SEESOIL* **6**, 2–38.

HARRIS, J.A., BIRCH, P. and SHORT, K.C. (1989). Changes in the microbial community and physico-chemical characteristics of topsoils stockpiled during opencast mining. *Soil Use and Management* **5**, 161–168.

HART, C.E. (1966). *Royal forest. History of Dean's woods as producers of timber.* Oxford University Press, London.

HAY, R. (In preparation). Forest road design. Forestry Commission Guide. Forestry Commission, Edinburgh.

HILTON, K.J. (ed.) (1967). *The Lower Swansea Valley Project.* Longmans Press, London.

HODGSON, D.R. and BUCKLEY, G.P. (1975). A practical approach towards the establishment of trees and shrubs on pulverised fuel ash. *In:* M.J. CHADWICK, and G.T. GOODMAN, eds. *Ecology of resource degradation and renewal.* Blackwell, Oxford, pp. 305–329.

HODGSON, D.R. and TOWNSEND, W.N. (1973). The amelioration and revegetation of pulverised fuel ash. *In:* R.J. HATRIK and G. DAVIES, eds. *Ecology and reclamation of devastated land.* Gordon and Breech, London, pp. 247–271.

HODGSON, J.M. (ed.) (1976). Soil survey field handbook. *Soil Survey Technical Monograph 5.* Harpenden.

HOOK, D.D., MURRAY, M.D., DeBELL, D.S. and WILSON, B.C. (1987). Variation in growth of red alder families in relation to shallow water table levels. *Forest Science* **33**, 224–229.

ICRCL (1987). *Guidance on the assessment and redevelopment of contaminated land.* ICRCL Guidance Note 59/83, 2nd edition. Department of the Environment, London.

INSLEY, H. and BUCKLEY, G.P. (1980). Some aspects of weed control for amenity trees on man-made sites. *In: Proceedings of the conference on weed control in forestry, Nottingham University,* Association of Applied Biologists, 189–200.

JEFFERIES, R.A. (1981). Legumes for the reclamation of derelict and disturbed land. *Landscape Design* **81** (5), 39–41.

JOBLING, J. (1972). Trials of species on other soils: industrial waste sites. *Report on forest research, London 1972.* HMSO, London, 35–36.

JOBLING, J. (1973). Trials of species on other soils: industrial waste sites. *Report on forest research, London 1973.* HMSO, London, 40–41.

JOBLING, J. (1977). Coal tip review. *Report on forest research, London 1977.* HMSO, London, p. 14.

JOBLING, J. (1978). Difficult man-made sites. *Report on forest research, London 1978.* HMSO, London, p. 13.

JOBLING, J. (1979). Reclaimed colliery spoil. *Report on forest research, Edinburgh 1979.* HMSO, London, p. 14.

JOBLING, J. and CARNELL, R. (1985). *Tree planting in colliery spoil.* Research and Development Paper 136. Forestry Commission, Edinburgh.

JOBLING, J. and STEVENS, F.R.W. (1980). *Establishment of trees on regraded colliery spoil heaps.* Occasional Paper 7. Forestry Commission, Edinburgh.

JOBLING, J. and VARCOE, W.M. (1985). *Establishment and management of trees on reclaimed colliery spoil.* Unpublished final report to Department of the Environment. Forestry Commission, Farnham.

JOHNSON, M. (1989). Involving the public. *In:* B.G. HIBBERD, ed. *Urban forestry practice.* Forestry Commission Handbook 5. HMSO, London, pp. 26–34.

JOHNSON, M.S., PUTWAIN, P.D. and HOLLIDAY, R.J. (1978). Wildlife conservation value of derelict metalliferous mine workings in Wales. *Biological Conservation* **14**, 131–148.

KEMP, J. (1988). Observations on the effect of modern restoration techniques on stream flow at Outgang opencast coal site, Cumbria. *In: Ten years of research – what next?* British Coal, Newcastle, 26–36.

KNOX, K. (1989). Practice and trends in landfill in the UK. *In:* T.H. CHRISTENSEN, R. COSSU and R. STEGMANN, eds. *Sanitary landfilling: process, technology and environmental impacts.* Academic Press, London, pp. 533–548.

LA DELL, T. (1983). An introduction to tree and shrub seeding. *Landscape Design* **83** (8), 27–31.

LAND CAPABILITY CONSULTANTS (1989). *Cost effective management of reclaimed derelict sites.* HMSO, London.

LAND USE CONSULTANTS (1992). *Amenity reclamation of mineral workings.* HMSO, London.

LAVENDER, S.J. (1981). *New land for old.* Hilger, Bristol.

LINES, R. (1979). Airborne pollutant damage to vegetation – observed damage. *In: Sulphur emissions and the environment.* Society of the Chemical Industry, London, 234–241.

LUCAS, O.W.R. (1983). Design of landform and planting. *In: Reclamation of mineral workings to forestry.* Research and Development Paper 132. Forestry Commission, Edinburgh, 24–36.

LUKE, A., BROWN, D. and NILES, J. (1987). Successful sand pit revegetation with woody plants. *Professional Horticulture* **1**, 106–111.

LUKE, A.G.R. and MACPHERSON, T.K. (1983). Direct tree seeding: a potential aid to land reclamation in central Scotland. *Aboricultural Journal* **7**, 287–299.

MACAULAY LAND USE RESEARCH INSTITUTE (1988). *Land capability for forestry.* Sheet 6: South West Scotland. Forestry Commission, Edinburgh.

MAFF (MINISTRY OF AGRICULTURE, FISHERIES AND FOOD) (1981). *The analysis of agricultural materials.* MAFF Reference Book 427. HMSO, London.

MAITLAND, P.S., NEWSON, M.D. and BEST, G.A. (1990). The impact of afforestation and forestry practice on freshwater habitats. *Focus on Nature Conservation No. 23.* Nature Conservancy Council, Peterborough.

MARRS, R.H. and BRADSHAW, A.D. (1980). Ecosystem development on reclaimed china clay wastes. III. Leaching of nutrients. *Journal of Applied Ecology* **17**, 727–736.

McNEILL, J.D., HOLLINGSWORTH, M.K., MASON, W.L., MOFFAT, A.J., SHEPPARD, L.J. and WHEELER, C.T. (1989). *Inoculation of Alnus rubra seedlings to improve seedling growth and forest performance.* Research Information Note 144. Forestry Commission, Edinburgh.

McNEILL, J.D. and MOFFAT, A.J. (1992). Reclamation of upland sites. *Report on forest research, Edinburgh 1991.* HMSO, London, p.17.

METEOROLOGICAL OFFICE (1989). *Climatological data for agricultural land classification.* Meteorological Office, Bracknell.

MOFFAT, A.J. (1987). The geological input to the reclamation process in forestry. *In:* M.G. CULSHAW, F.G. BELL, J.C. CRIPPS and M. O'HARA, eds. *Planning and engineering geology.* Engineering Geology Special Publication 4. Geological Society, London, 541–548.

MOFFAT, A.J. (1989). *The establishment of trees on soil amended with gypsum.* First report to Central Electricity Research Laboratory. Forestry Commission, Farnham.

MOFFAT, A.J. (1991). *The establishment of trees on soil amended with gypsum.* Final report to National Power TEC. Forestry Commission, Farnham.

MOFFAT, A.J., BENDING, N.A.D. and ROBERTS, C.J. (1991). The use of sewage sludge as a fertiliser in the afforestation of opencast coal spoils in South Wales. *In:* M.C.R. DAVIES, ed. *Land reclamation. An end to dereliction?* Elsevier Applied Science, London, pp. 391–392.

MOFFAT, A.J. and HOUSTON, T.J. (1991). Tree establishment and growth at Pitsea landfill site, Essex, U.K. *Waste Management and Research* **9**, 35–46.

MOFFAT, A.J. and ROBERTS, C.J. (1989a). The use of sewage sludge in reclamation. *Report on forest research, Edinburgh 1989.* HMSO, London, p.27.

MOFFAT, A.J. and ROBERTS, C.J. (1989b). Experimental tree planting on china clay spoils in Cornwall. *Quarterly Journal of Forestry* **83**, 149–156.

MOFFAT, A.J. and ROBERTS, C.J. (1989c). The use of large scale ridge and furrow landforms in forestry reclamation of mineral workings. *Forestry* **62**, 233–248.

MOFFAT, A.J. and ROBERTS, C.J. (1990). Grass mixtures for afforested opencast spoils in South Wales. *Land Degradation and Rehabilitation* **2**, 127–134.

MOFFAT, A.J., ROBERTS, C.J. and McNEILL, J.D. (1989). *The use of nitrogen-fixing plants in forest reclamation.* Research Information Note 158. Forestry Commission, Edinburgh.

NATIONAL AUDIT OFFICE (1986). *Review of Forestry Commission objectives and achievements.* HMSO, London.

NATURE CONSERVANCY COUNCIL (1990). *Earth science conservation in Great Britain: a strategy.* Nature Conservancy Council, Peterborough.

NEUSTEIN, S.A. and JOBLING, J. (1965). Afforestation of difficult sites: industrial sites. *Report on forest research, London 1964.* HMSO, London, p. 21.

NEUSTEIN, S.A., EVERARD, J. and JOBLING, J. (1968). Afforestation of difficult sites: industrial sites. *Report on forest research, London 1968.* HMSO, London, 37–38.

NEUSTEIN, S.A. and JOBLING, J. (1969). Trials of species on other soils: industrial waste sites. *Report on forest research, London 1969.* HMSO, London, 50–51.

NEWTON, R.W.B. (1951). Afforestation of unrestored land. *Quarterly Journal of Forestry* **45**, 38–41.

PALANIAPPAN, V.M., MARRS, R.H. and BRADSHAW, A.D. (1979). The effect of *Lupinus arboreus* on the nitrogen status of china clay wastes. *Journal of Applied Ecology* **16**, 825–831.

PALMER, J.P. (1991). Techniques for reclaiming metalliferous tailings. *In:* M.C.R. DAVIES, ed. *Land reclamation. An end to dereliction?* Elsevier Applied Science, London, pp. 357–365.

PALMER, J.P., MORGAN, A.L. and WILLIAMS, P.J. (1985). Determination of the nitrogen composition of colliery spoil. *Journal of Soil Science* **36**, 209–217.

PEPPER, H.W. (1992). *Forest fencing.* Forestry Commission Bulletin 102. HMSO, London.

PINCHIN, R.D. (1951). Plantations on opencast ironstone mining areas in the Midlands. *Report on forest research, London 1951.* Forestry Commission, London, 31–34.

PINCHIN, R.D. (1953). *Afforestation of spoil heaps in the South Wales coalfield.* Unpublished departmental report. Forestry Commission, Farnham.

POTTER, C.J. (1989). Establishment and early maintenance. *In:* B.G. HIBBERD, ed. *Urban forestry practice.* HMSO, London, pp. 78–90.

POTTER, M.J. (1991). *Treeshelters.* Forestry Commission Handbook 7. HMSO, London.

PULFORD, I.D. (1991). A review of methods to control acid generation in pyritic coal mine wastes. *In:* M.C.R. DAVIES. ed. *Land reclamation. An end to dereliction?* Elsevier Applied Science, London, pp. 269–278.

PUTWAIN, P.D., EVANS, B.E. and KERRY, S. (1988). The early establishment of amenity woodland on roadsides by direct seeding. *Aspects of Applied Biology* **16**, 63–72.

PYATT, D.G. (1990). *Forest drainage.* Research Information Note 196. Forestry Commission, Edinburgh.

RADVANYI, A. (1980). Control of small mammal damage in the Alberta oil sands reclamation and afforestation program. *Forest Science* **26**, 687–702.

RAMSAY, W.J.H. (1986). Bulk soil handling for quarry restoration. *Soil Use and Management* **2**, 30–39.

REANEY, M. (1990). How green is my valley. *Forest Life* **7**, 10–11.

RICHARDSON, J.A. (1958). Temperature and growth on pit heaps. *Journal of Ecology* **46**, 537–546.

RIMMER, D.L. (1991). Soil storage and handling. *In:* P. BULLOCK and P.J. GREGORY, eds. *Soils in the urban environment.* Blackwell Scientific Publications, Oxford, pp. 76–86.

RMC (1987). *A practical guide to restoration.* RMC, Feltham.

ROBERTS, J. (1983). Forest transpiration: a conservative hydrological process? *Journal of Hydrology* **66**, 133–141.

ROTHWELL, R.L. (1971). Watershed management guidelines for logging and road construction. *Canadian Forestry Service Information Report* A–X–42. Edmonton.

ROWAN, A.A. (1976). *Forest road planning.* Forestry Commission Booklet 43. HMSO, London.

ROY WALLER ASSOCIATES LTD (1991). *Environmental effects of surface mineral workings.* HMSO, London.

RUARK, G.A., MADER, D.L. and TATTAR, T.A. (1983). The influence of soil moisture and temperature on the root growth and vigour of trees – a review. Part II. *Arboricultural Journal* **7**, 39–51.

SCOTTISH OFFICE (1990). *Scottish vacant land survey – commentary.* Unpublished Report.

SCULLION, J. (1991). Re-establishing earthworm populations on former opencast coal mining land. *In:* M.C.R. DAVIES, ed. *Land reclamation. An end to dereliction?* Elsevier Applied Science, London, pp. 377–386.

SCULLION, J., MOHAMMED, A.R.A. and RICHARDSON, H. (1988). The effect of storage and reinstatement procedures on earth-worm populations in soils affected by opencast mining. *Journal of Applied Ecology* **25**, 233–240.

SELMES, R.E. (1992). The British forest resource inventory and forecast. *In:* G.E. RICHARDS, ed. *Wood: fuel for thought.* Harwell Laboratories, Harwell, pp. 231–239.

SHELDON, J.C. and BRADSHAW, A.D. (1977). The development of a hydraulic seeding technique for unstable sand slopes. I. Effects of fertilisers, mulches and stabilisers. *Journal of Applied Ecology* **14**, 905–918.

STEELE, B.B. and GRANT, C.V. (1982). Topographic diversity and islands of natural vegetation: aids in re-establishing bird and mammal communities on reclaimed mines. *Reclamation and Revegetation Research* **1**, 367–381.

STEVENS, F.R.W., THOMPSON, D.A. and GOSLING, P.G. (1990). *Research experience in direct sowing for lowland plantation establishment.* Research Information Note 184. Forestry Commission, Edinburgh.

STREET, M. (1983). *The restoration of gravel pits for wildfowl.* ARC, Chipping Sodbury.

STREET, M. (1989). *Ponds and lakes for wildfowl.* Game Conservancy, Fordingbridge.

TAYLOR, C.M.A. (1987). Nutrition: sewage sludge. *Report on forest research, Edinburgh 1987.* HMSO, London, p. 24.

TAYLOR, C.M.A. (1991). *Forest fertilisation in Britain.* Forestry Commission Bulletin 95. HMSO, London.

TEASDALE, J.B. (1983). Forestry Commission and local authority liaison: the Minerals Act. *In: Reclamation of mineral workings to forestry.* Research and Development Paper 132. Forestry Commission, Edinburgh, pp. 3–5.

THORNES, J.B. (1980). Erosional processes of running water and their spatial and temporal controls: a theoretical viewpoint. *In:* M.J. KIRKBY and R.P.C. MORGAN, eds. *Soil erosion.* J. Wiley and Sons, Chichester, pp. 129–182.

THORNTON, I. (1980). Geochemical aspects of heavy metal pollution and agriculture in England and Wales. *In: Inorganic pollution and agriculture.* MAFF Reference Book 326. HMSO, London, pp. 105–125.

THORNTON, I. (1991). Metal contamination of soils in urban areas. *In:* P. BULLOCK and P.J. GREGORY, eds. *Soils in the urban environment.* Blackwell Scientific Publications, Oxford, pp. 47–75.

TOWNSEND, W.N. and HODGSON, D.R. (1973). Edaphological problems associated with deposits of pulverised fuel ash. *In:* R.J. HATRIK and G. DAVIES, eds. *Ecology and reclamation of devastated land.* Gordon and Breech, London, pp. 45–56.

UK CLIMATE CHANGE IMPACTS REVIEW GROUP (1991). *The potential effects of climate change in the United Kingdom.* HMSO, London.

VANN, A.R., BROWN, L., CHEW, E., DENISON SMITH, G. and MILLER, E. (1988). Early performance of four species of *Alnus* on derelict land in the industrial Pennines. *Quarterly Journal of Forestry* **82**, 165–170.

VOGEL, W.G. (1987). *A manual for training reclamation inspectors in the fundamentals of soils and revegetation.* U.S. Department of Agriculture: Forest Service, Kentucky.
WALKER, S. (1981). *The potential for woodland rehabilitation of derelict mined land on the United Downs, Cornwall, England.* Unpublished M.Sc. thesis. Camborne School of Mines, Cornwall.
WARDELL ARMSTRONG (1993). *Landscaping and revegetation of china clay wastes.* Department of the Environment, London.
WELSH OFFICE (1991). *Results of the survey of land for mineral workings in Wales.* Welsh Office, Cardiff.
WHITE, J. (1959). Afforestation of a former opencast coal site in Coed Morgannwg, South Wales. *Journal of the Forestry Commission,* **28**, 69–74.
WILLIAMSON, D.R. and LANE, P.B. (1989). *The use of herbicides in the forest.* Forestry Commission Field Book 8. HMSO, London.
WILLIAMSON, J.C. and JOHNSON, D.B. (1990). Mineralisation of organic matter in topsoils subjected to stockpiling and restoration at opencast coal sites. *Plant and Soil* **128**, 241–247.
WILSON, G. (1991). *Post closure problems on landfill sites.* Proceedings of a National Association of Waste Disposal Constractors training course on the practical landfill restoration and after-care of landfill sites. Welwyn, 18–19 April 1991.
WILSON, G. and THOMAS, R. (1991). The preservation of geological exposures in landfilled quarries. *In: Sardinia '91: third international landfill symposium proceedings.* Environmental Sanitary Engineering Centre, Cagliari, 1171–1178.
WILSON, K. (1985). *A guide to the reclamation of mineral workings for forestry.* Research and Development Paper 141. Forestry Commission, Edinburgh.
WILSON, K. (1987). Reclamation of mineral workings to forestry. *In:* D. PATCH, ed. *Advances in practical arboriculture.* HMSO, London, pp. 38–41.
WOLSTENHOLME, R., DUTCH, J., MOFFAT, A.J., BAYES, C.D. and TAYLOR, C.M.A. (1992). *A manual of good practice for the use of sewage sludge in forestry.* Forestry Commission Bulletin 107. HMSO, London.
WOOD, R.F., HOLMES, G.D. and FRASER, A.I. (1961). Afforestation of particular types of land. *Report on forest research, London 1960.* HMSO, London, p. 27.
WOOD, R.F. and THURGOOD, J.V. (1955). *Tree planting on colliery spoil heaps.* Research Branch Paper 17. Forestry Commission, London.
WRIGHT, P.J. (1989). Specialised machinery in land restoration. *M & Q Environment* **2**, 20–23.

Appendix 1

Forestry Authority grants

Woodland Grant Scheme

The Woodland Grant Scheme (WGS) was introduced in April 1988 to encourage the continued expansion of forestry, in a way which achieves a reasonable balance with the needs of the environment (Forestry Commission, 1991a). It offers grants for establishing new woodland, and also for managing established woodland; reclaimed mineral and derelict land is as eligible as undisturbed land, provided the reclamation is adequate to establish and maintain a tree crop.

The main relevant objectives of the scheme are:

- to encourage the creation of new forests and woodlands, which increase the production of wood, enhance the landscape, provide new habitats for wildlife and offer opportunities for sport and leisure
- to provide jobs and increase the economic potential of rural and other areas which have few alternative sources of economic activity
- to provide a use of land as an alternative to agriculture.

The scheme is intended to encompass a wide range of management objectives and thus encourage multiple-purpose woodland management. Timber production is now no longer an essential objective (Forestry Commission, 1991a). In the context of man-made sites, conditions may not permit the planting of usual forest tree species. Nevertheless, most tree species are now supported under the grant scheme, provided that they are silviculturally suited to the site, and appropriate to the management aims.

Application for an **establishment grant** under the WGS should be made to the local Forestry Authority Conservancy Office (see Appendix 4). The application form is normally assessed in conjunction with a site visit, which usually takes place after the restoration phase of mineral reclamation, so that the forest officer can examine the physical nature of the restored land to be planted. Nevertheless, early submission of a WGS application, even before mineral extraction, is beneficial – allowing early consultation over aspects of the reclamation process such as choice of soil materials and their final thickness, or the method of soil replacement.

After the application has been approved, the work specified in the Plan of Operations may be carried out. Seventy per cent of the grant is payable after planting has taken place, with further instalments of 20% and 10% payable at five yearly intervals thereafter, subject to satisfactory establishment and maintenance. Applicants are required to allow Forestry Authority officers access to the land at any reasonable time to inspect areas for which the grant has been claimed.

WGS **management grants** are intended as a contribution to the net cost of the management operations needed to maintain and improve woodlands and forests, in recognition of the resulting silvicultural, environmental and social benefits. Details of this grant are contained in the WGS Applicant's Pack.

Community Woodland Supplement

This grant is designed to give encouragement to the creation of woodlands near to towns and cities. Early opportunities for public access and woodland recreation are central to the award of the supplement. Tree planting on restored mineral workings and derelict land will be eligible provided these objectives can be met, and safety is duly considered. Details of this grant are available from Forestry Authority conservancy offices (see Appendix 4).

Appendix 2

Reclamation case study: Woorgreen restored opencast coal site, Forest of Dean, Gloucestershire

In the Forest of Dean, coal has long been extracted from deep mines. But in the last decade pressure for opencast operations has increased, and in the late 1970s permission for opencast coaling was sought for Woorgreen, an area of some 80 ha of Forestry Commission coniferous woodland south-west of Cinderford.

Before extraction was sanctioned, a restoration specification was drawn up, based on a comprehensive site survey. Existing geological and soil survey information was supplemented by borehole data and over 30 inspection pits, purposely dug to characterise soil-forming materials texturally and for stoniness and acidity. The survey data were used to construct a map showing both the thickness of topsoil to be lifted and the additional amounts of loamy or lighter textured subsoil which were to be reserved. Mottled grey and ochreous clays and soft shales were to be discarded as soil-forming materials wherever lighter textured overburden was available.

Operations began in August 1978, and the site was worked progressively from west to east, restoration following the extraction of coal in each phase. Despite the identification of moderately permeable soil-forming materials, restoration gradients over much of the Woorgreen site were planned to be less than 5°, with potential problems of waterlogging in winter months. To combat this, a series of 30 m wide ridges were constructed to give c. 5° slopes over most of the site. The restoration plan included the construction of a large area of open water in the centre of the site. This area was excluded from tree planting because it was a probable frost pocket, and also because a wetland wildlife habitat was considered a desirable element in the site restoration.

Compaction was relieved and permeability increased by cross-ripping down to 750 mm using designed winged tines mounted on a Caterpillar D8. An elevated planting position was created by drawing RCM discs along the same lines that the tines had followed. The spoils and soils were stabilised with grass/legume mixtures, and planted with European and hybrid larches, Corsican pine and common alder. Restoration operations were completed in July 1980.

Restoration has given the Woorgreen site much more visual character than it possessed before opencast mining (see Plate 7). In an area of almost continuous tree cover, the standing water and open ground habitats are especially valued for wildlife. Birds such as whinchat and tree pipit have colonised the open ground, helped by the large amount of gorse which quickly invaded. Other birds include stonechat, meadow pipit, skylark, cuckoo, sparrowhawk, kestrel and hobby.

In the wetland area, the muddy margins of the lake are valuable for passage waders such as spotted redshank, greenshank, green sandpiper, curlew and lapwing. The shallow sloping edges of the lake are ideal for dabbling ducks – mallard, teal, tufted duck, greylag goose, dabchick, moorhen and goldeneye have all been noted. The lake is now the Forest of Dean's best dragonfly site, on which 17 species are recorded. There are breeding populations of the scarce bluetailed damselfly, large red and azure damselflies, southern hawker, ruddy sympetrum, broad-bodied chaser and the emperor dragonflies.

Tree growth on the ridge and furrow landform has been very successful for a reclaimed site. The yield class (YC) for both larches and Corsican pine was assessed at YC 10 in 1991, close to the average YC for undisturbed sites in the region.

Appendix 3

Restoration and aftercare checklists

Restoration checklist

This includes information which a mineral operator might provide to mineral planning authorities in support of a planning application which includes the provision for reclamation to a forestry end-use. The list of items below is derived from Department of the Environment Minerals Planning Guidance Note 7 (1989) and should be treated as guidance only. Individual site conditions and reclamation objectives may dictate that other information is also required.

1. A copy of the relevant planning application and Section 27 certificates.
2. An Ordnance Survey plan of the area at 1:2500 indicating:
   - the outer boundaries of the area to be excavated;
   - the outer boundaries of the total site so that areas located for topsoil and subsoil can be seen; and
   - details of any existing topsoil, subsoil or soil-forming material mounds that may be used in the restoration, including position, types and quantities available.
3. Details of the type and depth of proposed workings and volumes of materials to be removed. Details resulting from geological or hydrological investigations including water-table levels, nature and thickness of soil-forming materials, and depth and nature of topsoils, subsoils and overburden.
4. A strategic plan of the type of reclamation to forestry that is proposed, including:
   - projected plan of contours and final levels of the site, together with information about soil-forming materials, subsoil and topsoil depths;
   - the phasing and time-scale of the working, restoration and aftercare;
   - the methods of filling, where appropriate; types of fill and materials proposed;
   - the methods of stripping, transporting and restoring soils, including schemes of soil and machine movement, where appropriate;
   - proposed outfalls for drainage of the restored land, and proposals for creation of any permanent water areas; and
   - proposed access roads.

Aftercare checklist

This includes guidance on aftercare scheme content (from Department of the Environment Minerals Planning Guidance Note 7, 1989)

1. A successful aftercare scheme for forestry requires details of all the steps that will be undertaken during the five year period, plus others that may become necessary as a result of steps such as foliar analysis.
2. An **initial programme** should be prepared, including all the actions necessary to plant and establish the tree crop. This should be submitted to the mineral planning authority not later than three months before aftercare is to begin.
3. The details need to be discussed and agreed by the mineral planning authority, the Forestry Authority, and the person(s) responsible for the conduct of the aftercare programme. The items to be included and level of detail required for each are discussed in paragraphs 6 to 13 of this checklist. The proposals need to take into account any relevant local circumstances, and will also conform to principles of good forestry practice.
4. The aftercare scheme should be accompanied by a map showing all the areas subject to aftercare management, and clearly identifying areas according to types of proposed management.
5. In subsequent years, an **annual programme** of maintenance procedures for the plantation(s) should be submitted to the mineral planning authority for approval, not less than one month before an annual aftercare site meeting. Commitments are likely to be drawn from the guidance in paragraphs 11 to 14 of this checklist, although, exceptionally, drainage may also need to be considered during this period of aftercare.

6. **Cultivation practices.** This should include an outline of the range of cultivations likely to be undertaken, including depth and timing of operations, and suggested machinery to be utilised.
7. **Secondary treatments.** Commitments to undertake secondary treatments, such as discing to form low planting ridges, need to be outlined.
8. **Drainage.** This should have been considered during the planning and execution of the restoration phase. However, if there is a perceived need for drainage during aftercare, the drainage design needs to be outlined, including a map of ditches, showing their location, depth, gradients and outfalls.
9. **Ground cover.** Where herbaceous ground cover is proposed, details of species composition, density of cover, and timing and method of establishment should be outlined.
10. **Tree planting.** Details of species, stock type and size, tree spacing, and the method, timing and position of planting are required. If mixtures of species are proposed, details of the proportion of individual species are needed, together with a ground plan showing how the mixture is to be planted. If individual tree protection is required, details should be included.
11. **Fertilisers.** The basis for determining the need for and application rate of fertilisers should be outlined, including method(s) of approach (e.g. soil and/or foliar analysis) and the timing of such investigations and operations.
12. **Weed control.** Details of intended weed control, including methods, chemical to be used, and timing should be included.
13. **Site maintenance.** Commitments to maintain tree stocking to an agreed density, and tree protection where appropriate, need to be outlined. There should also be a commitment to investigate and remedy site conditions which cause abnormal tree failure.
14. **Fencing.** Fencing is not covered by aftercare conditions. Erection of fencing and its subsequent maintenance need to be a separate condition of the planning permission.

Appendix 4

Forestry Commission Addresses

Scotland

Dumfries and Galloway Conservancy
134 High Street
Lockerbie
Dumfriesshire
DG11 2BX

Grampian Conservancy
Ordiquhill
Portsoy Road
Huntly
AB54 4SJ

Highland Conservancy
Hill Street
Dingwall
Ross-shire
IV15 8EP

Lothian and Borders Conservancy
North Wheatlands Mill
Wheatlands Road
Galashiels
TD1 2HQ

Perth Conservancy
10 York Place
Perth
PH2 9JP

Strathclyde Conservancy
21 India Street
Glasgow
G2 4PL

England

Cumbria and Lancashire Conservancy
Peil Wyke
Bassenthwaite Lake
Cockermouth
Cumbria
CA13 9YG

East Anglia Conservancy
Santon Downham
Brandon
Suffolk
IP27 0TJ

East Midlands Conservancy
Willingham Road
Market Rasen
Lincolnshire
LN8 3RQ

Greater Yorkshire Conservancy
Wheldrake Lane
Crockey Hill
York
YO1 4SG

Hampshire and West Downs Conservancy
Alice Holt
Wrecclesham
Farnham
Surrey
GU10 4LF

Kent and East Sussex Conservancy
Furnace Lane
Lamberhurst
Tunbridge Wells
Kent
TN3 8LE

Northumberland and Durham Conservancy
Redford
Hamsterley
Bishop Auckland
Co Durham
DL13 3NL

Thames and Chilterns Conservancy
The Old Barn
Upper Wingbury Farm
Wingrave
Aylesbury
Buckinghamshire
HP22 4RF

West Country Conservancy
The Castle
Mamhead
Exeter
Devon
EX6 8HD

West Midlands Conservancy
Rydal House
Colton Road
Rugeley
Staffordshire
WS15 3HF

Wye and Avon Conservancy
Bank House
Bank Street
Coleford
Gloucestershire
GL16 8BA

Wales
Mid Wales Conservancy
The Gwalia
Llandrindod Wells
Powys
LD1 6AA

North Wales Conservancy
Clawdd Newydd
Ruthin
Clwyd
LL15 2NL

South Wales Conservancy
Cantref Court
Brecon Road
Abergavenny
Gwent
NP7 7AX

Morgannwg Forest District
Resolven
Neath
West Glamorgan
SA11 4DR

Appendix 5

Specimen conditions for planning permission where forestry is the after-use

Soil stripping

1. Apart from tree felling, works to enclose the site and essential drainage works, no operations shall be carried out until topsoil, subsoil and shallow soil-forming materials have been fully stripped, either over the whole area of the site or over the first phase of an agreed soil stripping programme.
2. All topsoil shall be stripped to the full available depth from any part of the site before that part is excavated or is traversed by heavy vehicles or machinery (except for the purpose of stripping that part or stacking topsoil on that part), or is used for the erection of buildings, or for the stacking of subsoil or other overburden, or as a machinery dump or plant yard, or for the construction of a road.
3. All subsoil shall be stripped to the full available depth, and as a separate operation, before that part is excavated or otherwise used for the purposes described in Condition 2 above, excepting the stacking of subsoil.
4. Topsoil, subsoil and soil-forming materials shall only be stripped during the months May to September, when they are reasonably dry and friable and weather conditions are dry, unless otherwise agreed with the MPA in writing. In addition, unless otherwise agreed by the MPA, 3 clear days of dry weather shall have occurred prior to the stripping of any part of the site.
5. Dump truck and backactors shall be used to strip soils and soil-forming materials, and shall be controlled to minimise soil compaction, as may be agreed by the MPA.
6. On areas previously covered by trees, stumps and roots shall be pulled out and shaken to separate them from soils. The stumps, roots and brash shall be either burnt or buried, both in accordance with a scheme to be approved by the MPA.
7. The applicant shall give at least 7 days' notice to the MPA before soil stripping is to commence.
8. Sufficient topsoil, and subsoil shall be identified, stripped and stored to ensure that a minimum combined thickness of 1000 mm is available for subsequent replacement uniformly over all areas to be restored to a forestry after-use. If insufficient soils are available from surface layers to achieve this thickness, then the most suitable soil-forming materials shall be identified and recovered during the stripping and excavation operations, and these materials shall be stored for the subsequent restoration of the site.
9. Topsoil of such differing qualities that they require special consideration shall be stripped and stored separately.

Soil storage

1. Topsoil, subsoil and soil-forming materials shall be stored in separate storage mounds which do not overlap. None of these materials shall be removed from site.
2. Topsoil storage mounds shall be constructed with the minimum compaction, only that necessary to ensure stability, and, unless otherwise agreed by the MPA, shall not exceed 5 m in height.
3. Subsoil and soil-forming material storage mounds shall also be constructed with only the minimum amount of compaction necessary to ensure stability, and, unless otherwise agreed by the MPA, shall not exceed 6 m in height.
4. Storage mounds of topsoil, subsoil and soil-forming materials shall not be traversed by vehicles or machinery except during construction or removal of these mounds.
5. As soon as any individual mound is formed, the surface of the soils shall be lightly graded so as to restrict the ingress of surface water and/or groundwater into the stored soils. The ingress of surface water and/or groundwater to the mounds shall be restricted by the provision of cut-off drains excavated upslope of the storage mounds.
6. All mounds shall be seeded to grass within 3 months of their construction, and shall be so maintained until the soils are required for use in

the restoration of the site, except as may otherwise be agreed by the MPA. Weeds shall be controlled by cutting or herbicides.

7. Soils shall be protected at all times from contamination by *inter alia* oils, greases or other lubricants, fuel oil or overburden.
8. Within 3 months of the formation of any soil storage mound, the MPA shall be supplied with a plan showing the location of each mound, and the area of land from which the soils contained therein were stripped, together with a statement as to what quantity of material is contained in each mound.

Restoration plan

1. Within 6 months of the date of this permission, or within such other period as may be granted by the MPA in writing, a detailed scheme in respect of the final landform and restoration of the site suitable for forestry use shall be submitted to the MPA, showing the following information:

   a. the final contours of the site;

   b. the position and dimensions of any roads, tracks or rights of way to be retained or constructed;

   c. the position and dimensions of any ditches or watercourses to be provided or retained together with details of any armouring. Gradients to be stated if not evident from contour information;

   d. the position and details of any culverts, spillways or other permanent drainage features;

   e. the position and details of any water feature to be retained or created;

   f. the position and dimensions of any drainage berms together with details of the intended longitudinal gradient of such berms;

   g. the position and volume of all soil storage mounds;

   h. the proposed distribution of soil materials to be replaced; and

   i. the position and details of all fences, gates, cattle grids to be retained or provided.
2. Notwithstanding the generality of Condition 1 above, restoration shall make provision for the detailed requirements set out in Conditions 3 to 13 below.
3. On completion of restoration, all plant, machinery, buildings, fixed equipment, areas of hardstanding, including site compounds, and access and haul roads shall be removed unless otherwise agreed by the MPA.
4. All settlement ponds and lagoons shall, unless to be retained in accordance with approved plans, be emptied of water and slurry, any impounding banks shall be breached, and the voids shall be filled with dry inert material to approved levels.
5. Progressive and even backfilling of overburden shall be carried out during the period of mineral extraction in accordance with the approved plan, unless otherwise agreed by the MPA.
6. The replaced overburden shall be levelled and graded in accordance with the approved restoration contour plan and the restored site shall conform with the plan finally agreed in accordance with Condition 1 above, and shall be free from risk of ponding or erosion, and be free from hollows, mounds or other obstructions to the extraction of timber.
7. Following the replacement of the overburden, and before the replacement of the topsoil, the upper layers of the overburden shall be ripped downslope with a heavy duty winged subsoiler to a minimum depth of 600 mm spaced at no more than 1200 mm centres.
8. All stones and other impediments exceeding 300 mm in any one direction, and other deleterious foreign material exposed including wire rope and cable, shall be removed, and either carted off the site or buried on the site so as to be a minimum of 1 m below the overburden restoration surface.
9. Prior to any replacement of soil or soil-forming materials, all roads, tracks and contour berms shall, wherever practicable, be constructed, and wherever possible these features should be incorporated into the routes for transporting soils from storage mounds to the respreading sites.
10. All operations involving soil replacement shall only be carried out when the full volume of soil involved is in a suitably dry soil moisture condition, or conditions are otherwise judged to be suitable by the MPA.
11. Soil-forming materials, subsoil and topsoil shall be respread in ascending order in separate layers. Shovel and dumptruck operations shall be employed to load and transport soil materials. Vehicles transporting soils shall only travel along defined routes on the overburden surface. The spreading of soils shall be carried out by a

360° tracklaying excavator which shall not travel on the soils being placed. If, for whatever reason, compaction does occur then such layers shall be cultivated to relieve compaction, to the full depth of the layer plus 150 mm into the underlying layer using a winged tine subsoiler. Seven days' notice of the intention to spread soil materials shall be given to the MPA, to allow for inspection of the area.

Aftercare

1. An aftercare scheme, comprising such steps as may be necessary to bring the land to the required standard for forestry use, shall be submitted for the approval of the MPA in consultation with the Forestry Commission, not later than 6 months prior to the date on which it is expected that any restoration works shall be completed.
2. The submitted aftercare scheme shall specify the steps to be taken and the periods during which they are to be taken. Thereafter, the aftercare of the area restored shall be carried out in accordance with the aftercare scheme, as approved or modified, or as may subsequently be agreed by the MPA.
3. Notwithstanding the generality of Condition 2 above, aftercare shall include details such as:

a. the date on which the 5 year aftercare period is to commence;

b. the range of cultivations likely to be undertaken, including depth and timing of operations;

c. seeding to grass, including species composition, density of cover, and timing and method of establishment;

d. tree species, stock type and size, and spacing, method, timing and position of planting;

e. application of herbicides or other methods of controlling weeds;

f. application of fertilisers, or methods of determining fertiliser requirements;

g. forest management, including maintaining tree stocks to agreed densities, and commitment to investigate and remedy site conditions which cause abnormal tree failure;

h. maintenance of all drainage facilities, and any wetland features provided;

i. timing and frequency of inspections;

j. arrangements for submission of a report detailing an annual programme of procedures to maintain the plantation; and

k. arrangements for consultations with land owners or occupiers.

Appendix 6

Useful addresses

Agricultural Genetics Company Limited
Microbio Division
Church Street
Thriplow
Royston
Hertfordshire
SG8 7RE

Association of Professional Foresters
7–9 West Street
Belford
Northumberland
NE70 7QA

Countryside Council for Wales
Plas Penrhos
Ffordd Penrhos
Bangor
Gwynedd
LL57 2LQ

Department of the Environment
2 Marsham Street
London
SW1P 3EB

English Nature
Northminster House
Peterborough
PE1 1UA

The Forestry Authority
Research Advisory Service
Alice Holt Lodge
Wrecclesham
Farnham
Surrey
GU10 4LH

The Forestry Authority
Research Advisory Service
Northern Research Station
Roslin
Midlothian
EH25 9SY

The Horticultural Trades' Association
19 High Street
Theale
Reading
Berkshire
RG7 5AH

Institute of Chartered Foresters
7a St Colme Street
Edinburgh
EH3 6AA

Institution of Civil Engineers
1–7 Great George Street
London
SW1P 3AA

Institute of Ecology and Environmental Management
36 Kingfisher Court
Hambridge Road
Newbury
Berkshire
RG14 5SJ

Institute of Professional Soil Scientists
The Manor House
Castle Street
Spofforth
Harrogate
HG3 1AR

Royal Forestry Society of England, Wales and Northern Ireland
102 High Street
Tring
Hertfordshire
HP23 4AN

Royal Scottish Forestry Society
62 Queen Street
Edinburgh
EH2 4NA

Scottish Natural Heritage
12 Hope Terrace
Edinburgh
EH9 2AS

Scottish Office
St Andrew's House
Edinburgh
EH1 3DG

Welsh Office
Cathays Park
Cardiff
CF1 3NQ

Appendix 7

Calculation of thickness of soil for soil replacement

Calculation of soil thickness is based on average annual summer rainfall data (available for England and Wales only) (Meteorological Office, 1989). This is then amended to take account of the rainfall interception commonly presented by mature tree canopies. A value of 25% was chosen, representing an average figure for both broadleaves and conifers. After reducing the annual summer rainfall by the interception factor, the effective rainfall was compared with the evaporation of tree crops. A value of 350 mm was used as typical of both broadleaves (Hall and Roberts, 1990) and conifers (Roberts, 1983). The difference between rainfall inputs and evaporation demands was translated into soil thickness, depending on available water capacities given by Hodgson (1976). To determine the minimum soil thickness for stony soils, a stoniness of 30% by volume was used.

Several assumptions must be made in modelling minimum soil thicknesses from rainfall data.

- No run-off occurs during summer rainfall episodes. If run-off occurs, it reduces the amount of effective rainfall able to replenish soil moisture levels, and estimates of minimum soil thickness will be too low.
- Soils under mature tree canopies return to field capacity during each winter. This condition is unlikely to be met in dry years.
- Trees can ramify into, and extract water from, the total thickness of soil indicated by the model. If soils are poorly structured or compacted, moisture abstraction will be hindered, and drought effects felt.
- Future rainfall patterns will be similar to those used to calculate average annual summer rainfall (1941–70). Recent research on climatic change (UK Climate Change Impacts Review Group, 1991) suggests that this is unlikely, and has predicted hotter, drier summers. A drier climate will require a greater thickness of soil for moisture storage.
- Interception is independent of rainfall intensity. This is not strictly valid (Maitland *et al.*, 1990), but there is insufficient information available on this relationship to build into the model.

Appendix 8

Foliar sampling and analysis procedures (from Taylor, 1991)

Introduction

The foliage sampling procedure described below is designed primarily for conifers, but also includes reference to broadleaves.

It must be stressed that foliar analysis is not an infallible guide to achieving a financially optimum fertiliser strategy. Soil type, current tree growth and appearance, past fertiliser treatment, woodland stage, species and local experience are all important factors to be considered in deciding whether to fertilise.

At present, foliar sampling should be restricted to stands up to 4 m mean height.

Identification of areas to sample

Foliar analysis results will be easier to interpret if the sampling programme is designed to examine specific problems.

The crop to be sampled should be subdivided into areas of good and poor growth. Foliar samples should be taken from both these areas. Ideally, several sets of composite samples should be collected from each category to improve accuracy of results.

Timing of sampling

Samples may be collected at any time of day from the first week in October to the end of the second week in November. Deciduous conifers and broadleaves should be sampled in late July or August, after shoot growth is complete and before needles or leaves begin to change colour.

It is desirable to avoid sampling after periods of prolonged rain because nutrients, particularly potassium, may leach from the needles or leaves.

Selection of trees to sample

Five dominant and co-dominant trees should be sampled to form a composite set of samples from each category.

Age of foliage

Only shoots of the current year should be taken; needles or leaves should not be stripped off the shoot.

Position of sample shoot

On conifers, sample shoots should be taken from the first whorl below the leader, excluding any lammas growth; one shoot is taken per tree. Undamaged, fully expanded leaves should be collected from the outside of the crown of broadleaved trees. Shoots or leaves must be fully exposed to sunlight as shading affects the nutrient content.

Size of sample

Five sample shoots from conifers is usually sufficient for analysis, irrespective of the growth rate of the trees sampled. Where shoots are too long to fit in the polythene bag, they should be carefully cut in two. About 100 cm^3 of leaves, excluding the petioles, should be collected from broadleaved trees.

Packing, labelling and dispatch of samples

Samples should be shaken if wet, and then packed into 250 mm x 350 mm polythene bags. A label must be included detailing the location of the sampling area, species and planting year.

The bag of shoots from five trees should be rolled up and secured with a moderately tight elastic band.

Before dispatch a list of the samples submitted must be included, which confirms the information contained on the labels, plus the name and address of the sender, date of dispatch and analysis required (usually macronutrients).

If samples are to be sent to the Forestry Authority Foliar Analysis Service, they should be addressed:

Environmental Research Branch
The Forestry Authority
Research Division
Alice Holt Lodge
Wrecclesham, Farnham
Surrey GU10 4LH

The outside of the parcel should be marked 'Plant material – urgent'.

Appendix 9

Trigger concentrations for selected inorganic contaminants (from ICRCL, 1987)

Conditions

1. This table is invalid if reproduced without the conditions and footnotes
2. All values are for concentrations determined on spot samples based on adequate site investigation carried out prior to development. They do not apply to analysis of averaged, bulked or composited samples, nor to sites which have already been developed. All proposed values are tentative.
3. The lower values in Group A are similar to the limits for metal content of sewage sludge applied to agricultural land. The values in Group B are those above which phytotoxicity is possible.
4. If all sample values are below the **threshold** concentrations then the site may be regarded as uncontaminated as far as the hazards from these contaminants are concerned and development may proceed. Above the **action** concentrations, remedial action may be needed, especially if the contamination is still continuing. Above the **action** concentration, remedial action will be required or the form of development changed.

Group A: Contaminants which may pose hazards to health

Contaminant	*Planned use*	*Threshold*	*Action*
Arsenic	Domestic gardens, allotments	10	*
	Parks, playing fields, open space	40	*
Cadmium	Domestic gardens, allotments	3	*
	Parks, playing fields, open space	15	*
Chromium (hexavalent)[1]	Domestic gardens, allotments	25	*
	Parks, playing fields, open space	25	*
Chromium (total)	Domestic gardens, allotments	600	*
	Parks, playing fields, open space	1000	*
Lead	Domestic gardens, allotments	500	*
	Parks, playing fields, open space	2000	*
Mercury	Domestic gardens, allotments	1	*
	Parks, playing fields, open space	20	*
Selenium	Domestic gardens, allotments	3	*
	Parks, playing fields, open space	6	*

(*continued*)

Group B: Contaminants which are phytotoxic but not normally hazards to health

Contaminant	*Planned use*	*Threshold*	*Action*
Group B: Contaminants which are phytotoxic but not normally hazards to health			
Boron (water-soluble)[3]	Any uses where plants are to be grown[2, 6]	3	*
Copper[4, 5]	Any uses where plants are to be grown[2, 6]	130	*
Nickel[4, 5]	Any uses where plants are to be grown[2, 6]	70	*
Zinc[4, 5]	Any uses where plants are to be grown[2, 6]	300	*

Notes:

* Action concentrations will be specified in the next edition of ICRCL 59/83.

1 Soluble hexavalent chromium extracted by 0.1M HCl at 37° C; solution adjusted to pH 1.0 if alkaline substances present.

2 The soil pH value is assumed to be about 6.5 and should be maintained at this value. If the pH falls, the toxic effects and the uptake of these elements will be increased.

3 Determined by standards ADAS methods (soluble in hot water).

4 Total concentration (extractable by $HNO_3/HCl0_4$).

5 The phytotoxic effects of copper, nickel and zinc may be additive. The trigger values given here are those applicable to the 'worst-case'; phytotoxic effects may occur at these concentrations in acid, sandy soils. In neutral or alkaline soils phytotoxic effects are unlikely at these concentrations.

6 Grass is more resistant to phytotoxic effects than are most other plants and its growth may not be adversely affected at these concentrations.

Appendix 10

Tentative trigger concentrations for contaminants associated with former coal combustion sites (from ICRCL, 1987)

Conditions

1. This table is invalid if reproduced without the conditions and footnotes.
2. All values are for concentrations determined on spot samples based on adequate site investigation carried out prior to development. They do not apply to analysis of averaged, bulked or composited samples, nor to sites which have already been developed.
3. Many of these values are preliminary and will require regular updating. They should not be applied without reference to the current edition of the report *Problems arising from the development of gas works and similar sites.*
4. If all sample values are below the **threshold** concentrations then the site may be regarded as uncontaminated as far as the hazards from these contaminants are concerned, and development may proceed. Above these concentrations, remedial action may be needed, especially if the contamination is still continuing. Above the **action** concentrations, remedial action will be required or the form of development changed.

Contaminants	*Proposed uses*	*Threshold*	*Action*
Polyaromatic hydrocarbons[1, 2]	Domestic gardens, allotments, play areas	50	500
	Landscaped areas	1000	10 000
Phenols	Domestic gardens, allotments	5	200
	Landscaped areas	5	1000
Free cyanide	Domestic gardens, allotments	25	500
	Landscaped areas		
Complex cyanides	Domestic gardens, allotments	250	1000
	Landscaped areas	250	5000
Thiocyanate[2]	All proposed uses	50	NL
Sulphate	Domestic gardens, allotments	2000	10 000
	Landscaped areas		
Sulphide	All proposed uses	250	1000
Sulphur	All proposed uses	5000	20 000
Acidity (pH less than)	Domestic gardens, allotments	pH5	pH3
	Landscaped areas		

Notes

NL No limit set as the contaminant does not pose a particular hazard for this use.

[1] Used here as a marker for coal tar, for analytical reasons. See *Problems arising from the redevelopment of gasworks and similar sites*, Annex A1.

[2] See *Problems arising from the redevelopment of gasworks and similar sites* for details of analytical methods.

Appendix 11

Assessment of lime requirement in pyritic soils and spoils

Sampling soils and spoils

Samples should be representative of the area where tree planting is proposed, or of the overburden which may serve as a soil-forming material. Before sampling, the entire site or extent of the overburden should be inspected. Areas that are obviously different from others in appearance and vegetation cover should be sampled as individual units. A recommended method of sampling is to make a composite sample from several randomly collected subsamples in each visually distinct unit or type of soil. The number of subsamples needed for the composite sample will depend on the size of the unit and the variability of the materials within the unit. In areas where soils are already replaced, sampling should extend to the full depth in which rooting is anticipated.

Estimation of the potential acidity (following Colbourn, 1980)

Samples for analysis should be air-dried, and separated into greater than and less than 2 mm material. The greater than 2 mm material should be crushed until it passes the 2 mm sieve.

A 0.5 g sample should be weighed into a graduated 15 cm^3 pyrex centrifuge tube. The sample should be mixed with 7 cm^3 5M hydrochloric acid, and heated for 30 minutes in a boiling water bath, cooled, and the solution made up to 10 cm^3 and decanted. At this stage, the mineral residue in the tube must be washed thoroughly by adding distilled water, mixing, centrifuging and then discarding the liquid, and repeating this sequence three times. Three cm^3 of 2M nitric acid is then added to the residue, and the mixture must be shaken at room temperature for 10 minutes. Two cm^3 of 2M sodium hydroxide is then added to quench any reaction, and the solution is made up to 10 cm^3 with dilute hydrochloric acid, and then mixed thoroughly and centrifuged at 1000 g for three minutes. The supernatent, decanted off, is used for the determination of partial oxidation pyrite (POP) by atomic absorption spectrophotometry, and the result expressed in mM kg^{-1}.

Estimation of annual lime requirement

The partial oxidation pyrite content is used to determine annual lime requirement as follows:

mMoles of hydrogen ions produced annually by pyrite oxidation (HPA) = 2.9 + 5.17 (POP)

HPA can be neutralised by 500 HPA.x.y kg $CaCO_3$ $ha^{-1} yr^{-1}$,

where x is thickness of soil that soil sample represents (in metres),

and y is soil density (g cm^{-3}).

Index

ABOUT HMSO's STANDING ORDER SERVICE

The Standing Order service, open to all HMSO account holders*, allows customers to receive automatically the publications they require in a specified subject area, thereby saving them the time, trouble and expense of placing individual orders.

Customers may choose from over 4000 classifications arranged in more than 250 sub groups under 30 major subject areas. These classifications enable customers to choose from a wide range of subjects those publications which are of special interest to them. This is a particularly valuable service for the specialist library or research body. All publications will be despatched to arrive immediately after publication date. A special leaflet describing the service in detail may be obtained on request.

Write to PC11C1, Standing Order Service, HMSO Books, PO Box 276, LONDON SW8 5DT quoting classification reference 2103011 to order future titles in this series.

*Details of requirements to open an account can be obtained from PC32A, HMSO Books, PO Box 276, London SW8 5DT.

Printed in the UK for HMSO
Dd 0294475 4/94 C25 552 12521